SO-BWY-328

Mr. DOOLEY:

In the Hearts of His Countrymen

Mr. DOOLEY
In the Hearts of His Countrymen

GREENWOOD PRESS, PUBLISHERS
NEW YORK

TO

SIR GEORGE NEWNES, Bart.

Messrs. GEORGE ROUTLEDGE & SONS
LIMITED

AND OTHER PUBLISHERS WHO, UNINVITED, PRESENTED

MR. DOOLEY TO A PART OF THE BRITISH PUBLIC

1491314

PREFACE.

THE author may excuse the presentation of these sketches to the public on the ground that, if he did not publish some of them, somebody would, and, if he did not publish the others, nobody would. He has taken the liberty to dedicate the book to certain enterprising gentlemen in London who have displayed their devotion to a sentiment now widely prevailing in the Music Halls by republishing an American book without solicitation on the author's part. At the same time he begs to reserve *in petto* a second dedication to the people of Archey Road, whose secluded gayety he has attempted to discover to the world.

With the sketches that come properly under the title " Mr. Dooley : In the Hearts of His Countrymen " are printed a number that do not. It has seemed impossible to a man who is not a Frenchman, and who is, therefore, tremendously excited over the case, to avoid discussion of the Jabberwocky of the Rennes court-martial as it is reported in America and England. Mr. Dooley cannot lag behind his fellow Anglo-Saxons in this matter. It is sincerely to be hoped that his small contribution to the literature of the subject will at last open the eyes of France to the necessity of conducting her trials, parliamentary sessions, revolutions, and other debates in a language more generally understood in New York and London.

F. P. D.

DUBLIN, August 30, 1899.

CONTENTS.

CONTENTS

PAGE

Mr. DOOLEY:

In the Hearts of His Countrymen

EXPANSION.

"Whin we plant what Hogan calls th' starry banner iv Freedom in th' Ph'lippeens," said Mr. Dooley, "an' give th' sacred blessin' iv liberty to the poor, down-trodden people iv thim unfortunate isles,— dam thim! — we'll larn thim a lesson."

"Sure," said Mr. Hennessy, sadly, "we have a thing or two to larn oursilves."

"But it isn't f'r thim to larn us," said Mr. Dooley. "'Tis not f'r thim wretched an' degraded crathers, without a mind or a shirt iv their own, f'r to give lessons in politeness an' liberty to a nation that manny-facthers more dhressed beef than anny other imperyal nation in th' wurruld. We say to thim: 'Naygurs,' we say, 'poor, dissolute, uncovered wretches,' says we, 'whin th' crool hand iv Spain forged man'cles f'r ye'er limbs, as Hogan says, who was it crossed th' say an' sthruck off th' comealongs? We did, — by dad, we did. An' now, ye mis'rable, childish-minded apes, we propose f'r to larn

ye th' uses iv liberty.   In ivry city in this
unfair land we will erect school-houses an'
packin' houses an' houses iv correction; an'
we'll larn ye our language, because 'tis aisier
to larn ye ours than to larn oursilves yours.
An' we'll give ye clothes, if ye pay f'r thim;
an', if ye don't, ye can go without.   An',
whin ye're hungry, ye can go to th' morgue
— we mane th' resth'rant — an' ate a good
square meal iv ar-rmy beef.   An' we'll sind
th' gr-reat Gin'ral Eagan over f'r to larn ye
etiquette, an' Andhrew Carnegie to larn ye
pathriteism with blow-holes into it, an'
Gin'ral Alger to larn ye to hould onto a job;
an', whin ye've become edycated an' have all
th' blessin's iv civilization that we don't
want, that 'll count ye one.   We can't give
ye anny votes, because we haven't more thin
enough to go round now; but we'll threat ye
th' way a father shud threat his childher if
we have to break ivry bone in ye'er bodies.
So come to our ar-rms,' says we.

   " But, glory be, 'tis more like a rasslin'
match than a father's embrace.   Up gets

this little monkey iv an' Aggynaldoo, an'
says he, 'Not for us,' he says. 'We
thank ye kindly; but we believe,' he says,
'in pathronizin' home industhries,' he says.
'An,' he says, 'I have on hand,' he says, 'an'
f'r sale,' he says, 'a very superyor brand iv
home-made liberty, like ye'er mother used
to make,' he says. ''Tis a long way fr'm
ye'er plant to here,' he says, 'an' be th' time
a cargo iv liberty,' he says, 'got out here an'
was handled be th' middlemen,' he says, 'it
might spoil,' he says. 'We don't want
anny col' storage or embalmed liberty,' he
says. 'What we want an' what th' ol' re-
liable house iv Aggynaldoo,' he says, 'supplies to th' thrade,' he says, 'is fr-esh liberty r-right off th' far-rm,' he says. 'I
can't do annything with ye'er proposition,'
he says. 'I can't give up,' he says, 'th'
rights f'r which f'r five years I've fought
an' bled ivry wan I cud reach,' he says.
'Onless,' he says, 'ye'd feel like buyin' out
th' whole business,' he says. 'I'm a pathrite,' he says; 'but I'm no bigot,' he says.

"An' there it stands, Hinnissy, with th' indulgent parent kneelin' on th' stomach iv his adopted child, while a dillygation fr'm Boston bastes him with an umbrella. There it stands, an' how will it come out I dinnaw. I'm not much iv an expansionist mesilf. F'r th' las' tin years I've been thryin' to decide whether 'twud be good policy an' thrue to me thraditions to make this here bar two or three feet longer, an manny's th' night I've laid awake tryin' to puzzle it out. But I don't know what to do with th' Ph'lippeens anny more thin I did las' summer, befure I heerd tell iv thim. We can't give thim to anny wan without makin' th' wan that gets thim feel th' way Doherty felt to Clancy whin Clancy med a frindly call an' give Doherty's childher th' measles. We can't sell thim, we can't ate thim, an' we can't throw thim into th' alley whin no wan is lookin'. An' 'twud be a disgrace f'r to lave befure we've pounded these frindless an' on-grateful people into insinsibility. So I suppose, Hinnissy, we'll have to stay an' do th' best we can, an' lave Andhrew Carnegie secede fr'm th' Union. They'se wan consolation; an' that is, if th' American people can govern thimsilves, they can govern annything that walks."

"An' what 'd ye do with Aggy — whatd'ye-call-him?" asked Mr. Hennessy.

"Well," Mr. Dooley replied, with brightening eyes, "I know what they'd do with him in this ward. They'd give that pathrite what he asks, an' thin they'd throw him down an' take it away fr'm him."

A HERO WHO WORKED OVERTIME.

"WELL, sir," said Mr. Dooley, "it looks now as if they was nawthin' left f'r me young frind Aggynaldoo to do but time. Like as not a year fr'm now he'll be in jail, like Napoleon, th' impror iv th' Fr-rinch, was in his day, an' Mike, th' Burglar, an' other pathrites. That's what comes iv bein' a pathrite too long. 'Tis a good job, whin they'se nawthin' else to do; but 'tis not th' thing to wurruk overtime at. 'Tis a sort iv out-iv-dure spoort that ye shud engage in durin' th' summer vacation; but, whin a man carries it on durin' business hours, people begin to get down on him, an' afther a while they're ready to hang him to get him out iv th' way. As Hogan says, 'Th' las' thing that happens to a pathrite he's a scoundhrel.'

"Las' summer there wasn't a warmer pathrite annywhere in our imperyal dominions thin this same Aggynaldoo. I was with him mesilf. Says I: 'They'se a good

coon,' I says. 'He'll help us f'r to make
th' Ph'lippeens indepindint on us f'r sup-
port,' I says; 'an', whin th' blessin's iv civilization has been extinded to his beloved
counthry, an',' I says, 'they put up intarnal
rivinue offices an' post-offices,' I says, 'we'll
give him a good job as a letter-carrier,' I
says, 'where he won't have annything to
do,' I says, 'but walk,' I says.

"An' so th' consul at Ding Dong, th'
man that r-runs that end iv th' war, he says
to Aggynaldoo: 'Go,' he says, 'where glory
waits ye,' he says. 'Go an' sthrike a blow,'
he says, 'f'r ye'er counthry,' he says. 'Go,'
he says. 'I'll stay, but you go,' he says.
'They's nawthin' in stayin', an' ye might
get hold iv a tyrannical watch or a pocket
book down beyant,' he says. An' off wint
th' brave pathrite to do his jooty. He done
it, too. Whin Cousin George was pastin'
th' former hated Castiles, who was it stood
on th' shore shootin' his bow-an-arrow into
th' sky but Aggynaldoo? Whin me frind
Gin'ral Merritt was ladin' a gallant charge

again blank catredges, who was it ranged his
noble ar-rmy iv pathrites behind him f'r to
see that no wan attackted him fr'm th' sea
but Aggynaldoo? He was a good man thin,
— a good noisy man.

"Th' throuble was he didn't know whin
to knock off. He didn't hear th' wurruk
bell callin' him to come in fr'm playin' ball
an' get down to business. Says me Cousin
George: "Aggynaldoo, me buck,' he says,
'th' war is over,' he says, 'an' we've settled
down to th' ol' game,' he says. 'They're
no more heroes. All iv thim has gone to
wurruk f'r th' magazines. They're no more
pathrites,' he says. 'They've got jobs as
gov'nors or ar-re lookin' f'r thim or annything else,' he says. 'All th' prom'nint
saviors iv their counthry,' he says, 'but mesilf,' he says, 'is busy preparin' their definse,' he says. 'I have no definse,' he says;
'but I'm where they can't reach me,' he
says. 'Th' spoort is all out iv th' job; an',
if ye don't come in an' jine th' tilin masses
iv wage-wurrukers,' he says, 'ye won't even

have th' credit iv bein' licked in a gloryous
victhry,' he says. 'So to th' woodpile with
ye!' he says; 'f r ye can't go on cillybratin'
th' Foorth iv July without bein' took up f'r
disordherly conduct,' he says.

"An' Aggynaldoo doesn't undherstand it.
An' he gathers his Archery Club ar-round
him, an' says he: 'Fellow-pathrites,' he
says, 'we've been betrayed,' he says.
'We've been sold out without,' he says,
'gettin' th' usual commission,' he says.
'We're still heroes,' he says; 'an' our pitchers is in th' pa-apers,' he says. 'Go in,' he
says, 'an' sthrike a blow at th' gay deceivers,'
he says. 'I'll sell ye'er lives dearly,' he
says. An' th' Archery Club wint in. Th'
pathrites wint up again a band iv Kansas
sojers, that was wanst heroes befure they
larned th' hay-foot-sthraw-foot, an' is now
arnin' th' wages iv a good harvest hand all
th' year ar-round, an' 'd rather fight than ate
th' ar-rmy beef, an' ye know what happened.
Some iv th' poor divvles iv heroes is liber-
ated fr'm th' cares iv life; an' th' r-rest iv

thim is up in threes, an' wishin' they was home, smokin' a good see-gar with mother.

"An' all this because Aggynaldoo didn't hear th' whistle blow.   He thought th' boom was still on in th' hero business.   If he'd come in, ye'd be hearin' that James Haitch Aggynaldoo'd been appointed foorth-class postmasther at Hootchey-Kootchey; but now th' nex' ye know iv him 'll be on th' blotther at th' polis station: ' James Haitch Aggynaldoo, alias Pompydoor Jim, charged with carryin' concealed weepins an' ray-sistin' an officer.'   Pathriteism always dies when ye establish a polis foorce."

"Well," said Mr. Hennessy, "I'm kind iv sorry f'r th' la-ads with th' bows an' arrows.   Maybe they think they're pa-thrites."

"Divvle th' bit iv diff'rence it makes what they think, so long as we don't think so," said Mr. Dooley.   "It's what Father Kelly calls a case iv mayhem et chew 'em. That's Latin, Hinnissy; an' it manes what's wan man's food is another man's pizen."

RUDYARD KIPLING.

"I THINK," said Mr. Dooley, "th' finest pothry in th' wurruld is wrote be that frind iv young Hogan's, a man be th' name iv Roodyard Kipling. I see his pomes in th' pa-aper, Hinnissy; an' they're all right. They're all right, thim pomes. They was wan about scraggin' Danny Deever that done me a wurruld iv good. They was a la-ad I wanst knew be th' name iv Deever, an' like as not he was th' same man. He owed me money. Thin there was wan that I see mintioned in th' war news wanst in a while,— th' less we f'rget, th' more we ray-mimber. That was a hot pome an' a good wan. What I like about Kipling is that his pomes is right off th' bat, like me con-ver-sations with you, me boy. He's a minyit-man, a r-ready pote that sleeps like th' dhriver iv thruck 9, with his poetic pants in his boots beside his bed, an' him r-ready to jump out an' slide down th' pole th' minyit th' alarm sounds.

"He's not such a pote as Tim Scanlan,

that hasn't done annything since th' siege
iv Lim'rick; an' that was two hundherd
year befure he was bor-rn.   He's prisident
iv th' Pome Supply Company,— fr-resh
pothry delivered ivry day at ye'er dure.
Is there an accident in a grain illyvator?
Ye pick up ye'er mornin' pa-aper, an' they'se
a pome about it be Roodyard Kipling.   Do
ye hear iv a manhole cover bein' blown up?
Roodyard is there with his r-ready pen.
''Tis written iv Cashum-Cadi an' th' book
iv th' gr-reat Gazelle that a manhole cover
in anger is tin degrees worse thin hell.'   He
writes in all dialects an' anny language, plain
an' fancy pothry, pothry f'r young an' old,
pothry be weight or linyar measuremint,
pothry f'r small parties iv eight or tin a
specialty.   What's the raysult, Hinnissy?
Most potes I despise.   But Roodyard Kipling's pothry is aisy.   Ye can skip through
it while ye're atin' breakfuss an' get a c'rrect
idee iv th' current news iv th' day,— who
won th' futball game, how Sharkey is thrainin' f'r th' fight, an' how manny votes th'
pro-hybitionist got f'r gov'nor iv th' State iv

Texas.   No col' storage pothry f'r Kipling.
Ivrything fr-resh an' up to date.   All lays
laid this mornin'.

"Hogan was in to-day readin' Kipling's
Fridah afthernoon pome, an' 'tis a good
pome.   He calls it 'Th' Thruce iv th'
Bear.'   This is th' way it happened : Roodyard Kipling had just finished his mornin'
batch iv pothry f'r th' home-thrade, an' had
et his dinner, an' was thinkin' iv r-runnin'
out in th' counthry f'r a breath iv fr-resh
air, whin in come a tillygram sayin' that th'
Czar iv Rooshia had sint out a circular letther sayin' ivrybody in th' wurrld ought to
get together an' stop makin' war an' live a
quite an' dull life.   Now Kipling don't like
the czar.   Him an' th' czar fell out about
something, an' they don't speak.   So says
Roodyard Kipling to himsilf, he says :
'I'll take a crack at that fellow,' he says.
'I'll do him up,' he says.   An' so he
writes a pome to show that th' czar's letter's not on th' square.   Kipling's like me,
Hinnissy.   When I want to say annything
lib-lous, I stick it on to me Uncle Mike.

So be Roodyard Kipling. He doesn't come r-right out, an' say, 'Nick, ye're a liar!' but he tells about what th' czar done to a man he knowed be th' name iv Muttons. Muttons, it seems, Hinnissy, was wanst a hunter; an' he wint out to take a shot at th' czar, who was dhressed up as a bear. Well, Muttons r-run him down, an' was about to plug him, whin th' czar says, 'Hol' on,' he says,— 'hol' on there,' he says. 'Don't shoot,' he says. 'Let's talk this over,' he says. An' Muttons, bein' a foolish man, waited till th' czar come near him; an' thin th' czar feinted with his left, an' put in a right hook an' pulled off Muttons's face. I tell ye 'tis so. He jus' hauled it off th' way ye'd haul off a porous plasther,— raked off th' whole iv Muttons's fr-ront ilivation. 'I like ye'er face,' he says, an' took it. An' all this time, an' 'twas fifty year ago, Muttons hasn't had a face to shave. Ne'er a one. So he goes ar-round exhibitin' th' recent site, an' warnin' people that, whin they ar-re shootin' bears, they must see that their gun is kept loaded an' their face is nailed on

securely. If ye iver see a bear that looks
like a man, shoot him on th' spot, or, betther still, r-run up an alley. Ye must niver
lose that face, Hinnissy.

"I showed th' pome to Father Kelly,"
continued Mr. Dooley.

"What did he say?" asked Mr. Hennessy.

"He said," Mr. Dooley replied, "that I
cud write as good a wan mesilf; an' he took
th' stub iv a pencil, an' wrote this. Lemme
see — Ah! here it is : —

'Whin he shows as seekin' frindship with paws that're
     thrust in thine,
  That is th' time iv pearl, that is th' thruce iv th' line.

'Collarless, coatless, hatless, askin' a dhrink at th' bar,
  Me Uncle Mike, the Fenyan, he tells it near and far,

'Over an' over th' story : 'Beware iv th' gran' flimflam,
  There is no thruce with Gazabo, th' line that looks like
     a lamb.'

"That's a good pome, too," said Mr.
Dooley; "an' I'm goin' to sind it to th'
nex' meetin' iv th' Anglo-Saxon 'liance."

LORD CHARLES BERESFORD.

"I SEE be th' pa-apers," said Mr. Dooley, "that Lord Char-les Beresford is in our mist, as Hogan says."

"An' who th' divvle's he?" asked Mr. Hennessy.

"He's a Watherford man," said Mr. Dooley. "I knowed his father well,—a markess be thrade, an' a fine man. Char-les wint to sea early; but he's now in th' plastherin' business,—cemintin' th' 'liance iv th' United States an' England. I'll thank ye to laugh at me joke, Mr. Hinnissy, an' not be standin' there lookin' like a Chinnyman in a sthreet-car."

"I don't know what ye mean," said Mr. Hennessy, softly.

"Lord Charles Beresford is a sort iv advance agent iv th' White Man's Burden Thrajeedy Company,— two little Evas, four hundherd millyon Topsies, six hundherd millyon Uncle Toms. He's billin' the' counthry f'r th' threeyumphial tour iv th'

Monsther Aggregation. Nawthin' can stop it. Blood is thicker than wather; an' to-gether, ar-rm in ar-rm, we'll spread th' light iv civilization fr'm wan end iv th' wurruld to th' other, no matther what you an' Schwartz-meister say, Hinnissy.

"Be hivins, I like th' way me kinsmen acrost th' sea, as th' pa-apers say, threat us. 'Ye whelps,' says Lord Char-les Beresford an' Roodyard Kipling an' Tiddy Rosenfelt an' th' other Anglo-Saxons. 'Foolish an' frivolous people, cheap but thrue-hearted an' insincere cousins,' they says. ''Tis little ye know about annything. Ye ar-re a disgrace to humanity. Ye love th' dollar betther thin ye love annything but two dollars. Ye ar-re savage, but inthrestin'. Ye misname our titles. Ye use th' crool Krag-Jorgensen in-stead iv th' ca'm an' penethratin' Lee-Met-ford. Ye kiss ye'er heroes, an' give thim wurruk to do. We smash in their hats, an' illivate thim to th' peerage. Ye have de-sthroyed our language. Ye ar-re rapidly convartin' our ancesthral palaces into dwellin'-

houses.   Ye'er morals are loose, ye'er dhrinks
ar-re enervatin' but pleasant, an' ye talk
through ye'er noses.   Ye ar-re mussy at th'
table, an' ye have no religion.   But ye ar-re
whelps iv th' ol' line.   Those iv ye that ar-re
not our brothers-in-law we welcome as
brothers.   Ye annoy us so much ye must
be mimbers iv our own fam'ly.   Th' same
people that is washed occasionally be th'
Mississippi as it rowls majistic along th' im-
peeryal States iv Oheeho an' Duluth, wa-
thrin' th' fertyle plains iv Wyoming an'
Mattsachusetts, is to be found airnin' a
livin' on th' short but far more dirtier
Thames.   We have th' same lithrachoor.
Ye r-read our Shakspere so we can't undherstand it; an' we r-read ye'er aspirin'
authors, Poe an' Lowell an' Ol' Sleuth th'
Detective.   We ar-re not onfamilyar with
ye'er inthrestin' histhry.   We ar-re as pr-roud
as ye are iv th' achievements iv Gin'ral
Shafter an' Gin'ral Coxcy.   Ye'er ambass'-
dures have always been kindly received;
an', whether they taught us how to dhraw to

a busted flush or wept on our collars or re-
cited original pothry to us, we had a broth-
erly feelin' for thim that med us say, " Poor
fellows, they're doin' th' best they can."
' So,' says they, ' come to our ar-ams, an' together we'll go out an' conquer th' wurruld.'

" An' we're goin' to do it, Hinnissy. Th'
rayciption that this here sintimint has ray-
ceived fr'm ivry wan that has a son in col-
ledge is almost tumulchuse. We feel like a
long-lost brother that's been settin' outside
in th' cold f'r a week, an' is now ast in to
supper — an' sarched at th' dure f'r deadly
weepins. We'll have to set up sthraight an'
mind our manners. No tuckin' our nap-
kins down our throats or dhrinkin' out iv
th' saucer or kickin' our boots off undher
the table. No reachin' f'r annything, but
' Mah, will ye kindly pass th' Ph'lippeens?'
or ' No, thank ye, pah, help ye'ersilf first.'

" An' will we stay in ? Faith, I dinnaw.
We feel kindly to each other ; but it looks
to me like, th' first up in th' mornin', th'
first away with th' valu'bles."

"I'll niver come in," protested Mr. Hennessy, stoutly.

"No more ye will, ye rebelyous oma-dhon," said Mr. Dooley. "An' 'twas thinkin' iv you an' th' likes iv you an' Schwartzmeister an' th' likes iv him that med me wondher. If th' 'liance got into a war with Garmany, an' some wan was to start a rough-an'-tumble in Ireland about iliction time, I wondher wud th' cimint hold!"

HANGING ALDERMEN.

CHICAGO is always on the point of hanging some one and quartering him and boiling him in hot pitch, and assuring him that he has lost the respect of all honorable men. Rumors of a characteristic agitation had come faintly up Archey Road, and Mr. Hennessy had heard of it.

"I hear they're goin' to hang th' aldhermen," he said. "If they thry it on Willum J. O'Brien, they'd betther bombard him first. I'd hate to be th' man that 'd be called to roll with him to his doom. He cud lick th' whole Civic Featheration."

"I believe ye," said Mr. Dooley. "He's a powerful man. But I hear there is, as ye say, what th' pa-apers 'd call a movement on fut f'r to dec'rate Chris'mas threes with aldhermen, an' 'tis wan that ought to be encouraged. Nawthin' cud be happyer, as Hogan says, chin th' thought iv cillybratin' th' season be sthringin' up some iv th' fathers iv th' city where th' childher cud see thim.

But I'm afraid, Hinnissy, that you an' me won't see it. 'Twill all be over soon, an' Willum J. O'Brien 'll go by with his head just as near his shoulders as iver. 'Tis har-rd to hang an aldherman, annyhow. Ye'd have to suspind most iv thim be th' waist.

"Man an' boy, I've been in this town forty year an' more ; an' divvle th' aldherman have I see hanged yet, though I've sthrained th' eyes out iv me head watchin' f'r wan iv thim to be histed anny pleasant mornin'. They've been goin' to hang thim wan week an' presintin' thim with a dimon' star th' next iver since th' year iv th' big wind, an' there's jus' as manny iv thim an' jus' as big robbers as iver there was.

"An' why shud they hang thim, Hinnissy ? Why shud they ? I'm an honest man mesilf, as men go. Ye might have ye'er watch, if ye had wan, on that bar f'r a year, an' I'd niver touch it. It wudden't be worth me while. I'm an honest man. I pay me taxes, whin Tim Ryan isn't assessor with Grogan's boy on th' books. I do me jooty; an' I believe in th' polis foorce, though not in polismen. That's diff'rent. But honest as I am, between you an' me, if I was an aldherman, I wudden't say, be hivins, I think I'd stand firm; but — well, if some wan come to me an' said, ' Dooley, here's fifty thousan' dollars f'r ye'er vote to betray th' sacred inthrests iv Chicago,' I'd go to Father Kelly an' ask th' prayers iv th' congregation.

" 'Tis not, Hinnissy, that this man Yerkuss goes up to an aldherman an' says out sthraight, ' Here, Bill, take this bundle, an' be an infamyous scoundhrel.' That's th' way th' man in Mitchigan Avnoo sees it, but 'tis not sthraight. D'ye mind Dochney that was wanst aldherman here? Ye don't. Well, I do. He ran a little conthractin' business down be Halsted Sthreet. 'Twas him built th' big shed f'r th' ice comp'ny. He was a fine man an' a sthrong wan. He begun his political career be lickin' a plasthrer be th' name iv Egan, a man that had th' County

Clare thrip an' was thought to be th' akel iv
anny man in town. Fr'm that he growed
till he bate near ivry man he knew, an' become very pop'lar, so that he was sint to
th' council. Now Dochney was an honest
an' sober man whin he wint in; but wan day
a man come up to him, an' says he, 'Ye
know that ordhnance Schwartz inthrajooced?'
'I do,' says Dochney, 'an I'm again it.
'Tis a swindle,' he says. " Well,' says th'
la-ad, ' they'se five thousan' in it f'r ye,' he
says. They had to pry Dochney off iv him.
Th' nex' day a man he knowed well come
to Dochney, an' says he, 'That's a fine
ordhnance iv Schwartz.' 'It is, like hell,'
says Dochney. ' 'Tis a plain swindle,' he
says. ' 'Tis a good thing f'r th' comp'nies,'
says this man; ' but look what they've done
f'r th' city,' he says, ' an think,' he says,
' iv th widdies an' orphans,' he says, ' that
has their har-rd-earned coin invisted,' he
says. An' a tear rolled down his cheek.
'I'm an orphan mesilf,' says Dochney; 'an'
as f'r th' widdies, anny healthy widdy with

sthreet-car stock ought to be ashamed iv hersilf if she's a widdy long,' he says. An' th' man wint away.

"Now Dochney thought he'd put th' five thousan' out iv his mind, but he hadn't. He'd on'y laid it by, an' ivry time he closed his eyes he thought iv it. 'Twas a shame to give th' comp'nies what they wanted, but th' five thousan' was a lot iv money. 'Twud lift th' morgedge. 'Twud clane up th' notes on th' new conthract. 'Twud buy a new dhress f'r Mrs. Dochney. He begun to feel sorrowful f'r th' widdies an' orphans. 'Poor things!' says he to him- silf, says he. 'Poor things, how they must suffer!' he says; 'an' I need th' money. Th' sthreet-car comp'nies is robbers,' he says; 'but 'tis thrue they've built up th' city,' he says, 'an th' money'd come in handy,' he says. 'No wan 'd be hurted, annyhow,' he says; 'an', sure, it ain't a bribe f'r to take money f'r doin' something ye want to do, annyhow,' he says. 'Five thou- san' widdies an' orphans,' he says; an' he wint to sleep.

" That was th' way he felt whin he wint
down to see ol' Simpson to renew his notes,
an' Simpson settled it. ' Dochney,' he says,
' I wisht ye'd pay up,' he says. ' I need th'
money,' he says. ' I'm afraid th' council
won't pass th' Schwartz ordhnance,' he says;
' an' it manes much to me,' he says. ' Be
th' way,' he says, ' how're ye goin' to vote
on that ordhnance?' he says. ' I dinnaw,'
says Dochney. ' Well,' says Simpson
(Dochney tol' me this himsilf), 'whin ye
find out, come an' see me about th' notes,'
he says. An' Dochney wint to th' meetin';
an', whin his name was called, he hollered
' Aye,' so loud a chunk iv plaster fell out
iv th' ceilin' an' stove in th' head iv a
rayform aldherman.''

" Did they hang him?" asked Mr. Hen-
nessey.

" Faith, they did not," said Mr. Dooley.
" He begun missin' his jooty at wanst.
Aldhermen always do that after th' first few
weeks. ' Ye got ye'er money,' says Father
Kelly; ' an' much good may it do ye,' he

says. 'Well,' says Dochney, 'I'd be a long time prayin' mesilf into five thousan',' he says. An' he become leader in th' council. Th' las' ordhnance he inthrojooced was wan establishin' a license f'r churches, an' compellin' thim to keep their fr-ront dure closed an' th' blinds drawn on Sundah. He was expelled fr'm th' St. Vincent de Pauls, an' ilicted a director iv a bank th' same day.

"Now, Hinnissy, that there man niver knowed he was bribed — th' first time. Th' second time he knew. He ast f'r it. An' I wudden't hang Dochney. I wudden't if I was sthrong enough. But some day I'm goin' to let me temper r-run away with me, an' get a comity together, an' go out an' hang ivry dam widdy an' orphan between th' rollin' mills an' th' foundlin's' home. If it wasn't f'r thim raypechious crathers, they'd be no boodle anywhere."

"Well, don't forget Simpson," said Mr. Hennessy.

"I won't," said Mr. Dooley. "I won't."

THE GRIP.

Mr. Dooley was discovered making a seasonable beverage, consisting of one part syrup, two parts quinine, and fifteen parts strong waters.

"What's the matter?" asked Mr. McKenna.

"I have th' lah gr-rip," said Mr. Dooley, blowing his nose and wiping his eyes. "Bad cess to it! Oh, me poor back! I feels as if a dhray had run over it. Did ye iver have it? Ye did not? Well, ye're lucky. Ye're a lucky man.

"I wint to McGuire's wake las' week. They gave him a dacint sind-off. No porther. An' himsilf looked natural, as fine a corpse as iver Gavin layed out. Gavin tould me so himsilf. He was as proud iv McGuire as if he owned him. Fetched half th' town in to look at him, an' give ivry wan iv thim cards. He near frightened ol' man Dugan into a faint. 'Misther Dugan, how old a-are ye?' 'Sivinty-five, thanks be,' says Dugan. 'Thin,' says Gavin, 'take wan iv me cards,' he says. 'I hope ye'll not forget me,' he says.

"'Twas there I got th' lah grip. Lastewise, it is me opinion iv it, though th' docthor said I swallowed a bug. It don't seem right, Jawn, f'r th' McGuires is a clane fam'ly; but th' docthor said a bug got into me system. 'What sort iv bug?' says I. 'A lah grip bug,' he says. 'Ye have Mickrobes in ye'er lungs,' he says. 'What's thim?' says I. 'Thim's th' lah grip bugs,' says he. 'Ye took wan in, an' warmed it,' he says; 'an' it has growed an' multiplied till ye'er system does be full iv' thim,' he says, 'millions iv thim,' he says, 'marchin' an' counthermarchin' through ye.' 'Glory be to the saints!' says I. 'Had I better swallow some insect powdher?' I says. 'Some iv thim in me head has a fallin' out, an' is throwin' bricks.' 'Foolish man,' says he. 'Go to bed,' he says, 'an' lave thim alone,' he says. 'Whin they find who they're in,' he says, 'they'll quit ye.'

"So I wint to bed, an' waited while th' Mickrobes had fun with me. Mondah all iv thim was quite but thim in me stummick. They stayed up late dhrinkin' an' carousin' an' dancin' jigs till wurruds come up between th' Kerry Mickrobes an' thim fr'm Wexford; an' th' whole party wint over to me left lung, where they cud get th' air, an' had it out. Th' nex' day th' little Mickrobes made a toboggan slide iv me spine; an' manetime some Mickrobes that was wurkin' f'r th' tilliphone comp'ny got it in their heads that me legs was poles, an' put on their spikes an' climbed all night long.

"They was tired out th' nex' day till about five o'clock, whin thim that was in me head begin flushin' out th' rooms; an' I knew there was goin' to be doin's in th' top flat. What did thim Mickrobes do but invite all th' other Mickrobes in f'r th' ev'nin'. They all come. Oh, by gar, they was not wan iv them stayed away. At six o'clock they begin to move fr'm me shins to me throat. They come in platoons an' squads an' dhroves. Some iv thim brought along brass bands, an' more thin wan hundhred thousand iv thim dhruv through me pipes on dhrays. A throlley line was started up me back, an' ivry car run into a wagonload iv scrap iron at th' base iv me skull.

"Th' Mickrobes in me head must 've done thimsilves proud. Ivry few minyits th' kids 'd be sint out with th' can, an' I'd say to mesilf: 'There they go, carryin' th' thrade to Schwartzmeister's because I'm sick an' can't wait on thim.' I was daffy, Jawn, d'ye mind. Th' likes iv me fillin' a pitcher f'r a little boy-bug! Such dhreams! An' they had a game iv forty-fives; an' there was wan Mickrobe that larned to play th' game in th' County Tipp'rary, where 'tis played on stone, an' ivry time he led thrumps he'd like to knock me head off. 'Whose thrick is that?' says th' Tipp'rary Mickrobe. ''Tis mine,' says th' red-headed Mickrobe fr'm th' County Roscommon. They tipped over th' chairs an' tables: an', in less time thin it takes to tell, th' whole party was at it.

They'd been a hurlin' game in th' back iv me skull, an' th' young folks was dancin' breakdowns an' havin' leppin' matches in me forehead; but they all stopped to mix in. Oh, 'twas a grand shindig — tin millions iv men, women, an' childher rowlin' on th' flure, hands an' feet goin', ice-picks an' hurlin' sticks, clubs, brickbats, an' beer kags flyin' in th' air! How manny iv thim was kilt I niver knew; f'r I wint as daft as a hen, an' dhreamt iv organizin' a Mickrobe Campaign Club that 'd sweep th' prim'ries, an' maybe go acrost an' free Ireland. Whin I woke up, me legs was as weak as a day old baby's, an' me poor head impty as a cobbler's purse. I want no more iv thim. Give me anny bug fr'm a cockroach to an aygle save an' except thim West iv Ireland Fenians, th' Mickrobes."

1491314

LEXOW.

"THIS here wave iv rayform," said Mr. Dooley, "this here wave iv rayform, Jawn, mind ye, that's sweepin' over th' counthry, mind ye, now, Jawn, is raisin' th' divvle, I see be th' pa-apers. I've seen waves iv rayform befure, Jawn. Whin th' people iv this counthry gets wurruked up, there's no stoppin' thim. They'll not dhraw breath until ivry man that took a dollar iv a bribe is sent down th' r-road. Thim that takes two goes on th' comity iv th' wave iv rayform.

"It sthruck th' r-road las' week. Darcey, th' new polisman on th' bate, comes in here ivry night f'r to study spellin' an' figgers. I think they'll throw him down, whin he goes to be examined. Wan iv th' wild la-ads down be th' slough hit him with a brick wanst, an' he ain't been able to do fractions since. Thin he's got inflammathry rheumatism enough to burn a barn, an' he can't turn a page without makin' ye think he's goin' to lose a thumb. He's got wife an' childher, an' he's on in years; but he's a polisman, an' he's got to be rayformed. I tell him all I can. He didn't know where St. Pethersburg was till I tould him it was th' capital iv Sweden. They'll not give him th' boots on that there question. Ye bet ye'er life they won't, Jawn.

"I seen th' aldherman go by yisterdah; an' he'd shook his dimon'stud, an' he looked as poor as a dhrayman. He's rayformed. Th' little Dutchman that was ilicted to th' legislachure says he will stay home. Says I, 'Why?' Says he, 'There's nawthin' in it.' He's rayformed. Th' wather inspictor, that used to take a dhrink an' a segar an' report me two pipes less thin I have, turned me in las' week f'r a garden hose an' a ploonge bath. He's rayformed. Th' wave iv ray-form has sthruck, an' we're all goin' around now with rubbers on.

"They've organized th' Ar-rchey Road Lexow Sodality, an' 'tis th' wan institootion that Father Kelly up west iv th' bridge 'll duck his head to. All th' best citizens is in

it. Th' best citizens is thim that th' statue
iv limitations was made f'r. Barrister
Hogan tol' me — an' a dacint man, but give
to dhrink — that, whin a man cud hide behind th' statue iv limitations, he was all
r-right. I niver seen it. Is that th' wan on
th' lake front? No, tubby sure, tubby sure.
No wan 'd hide behind that.

" Th' Ar-rchey Road Lexow Sodality is
composed iv none but square men. They
all have th' coin, Jawn. A man that's
broke can't be square. He's got too much
to do payin' taxes. If I had a million,
divvle th' step would I step to confession.
I'd make th' soggarth come an' confess to
me. They say that th' sthreets iv Hivin was
paved with goold. I'll bet ye tin to wan
that with all th' square men that goes there
ivry year they have ilecloth down now."

" Oh, go on," said Mr. McKenna.

" I was goin' to tell ye about th' Lexow
Sodality. Well, th' chairman iv it is
Doherty, th' retired plumber. He sold me
a house an' lot wanst, an' skinned me out iv

wan hundherd dollars. He got th' house an' lot back an' a morgedge. But did ye iver notice th' scar on his nose? I was r-rough in thim days. Ol' Mike Hogan is another mimber. Ye know him. They say he hires constables be th' day f'r to serve five days' notices. Manny's th' time I see th' little furniture out on th' sthreet, an' th' good woman rockin' her baby under th' open sky. Hogan's tinants. Ol' Dinnis Higgins is another wan. An' Brannigan, th' real estate dealer. He was in th' assissors' office. May Gawd forgive him! An' Clancy, that was bail-bondman at Twelfth Sthreet.

"They appointed comities, an' they held a meetin'. I wint there. So did some iv th' others. 'Twas at Finucane's, an' th' hall was crowded. All th' sodality made speeches. Doherty made a great wan. Th' air was reekin' with corruption, says he. Th' polis foorce was rotten to th' core. Th' rights iv property was threatened. What, says he, was we goin' to do about it?

"Danny Gallagher got up, as good a lad

as iver put that in his face to desthroy
his intelligence, as Shakspere says. 'Gintlemen,' says he, 'wan wurrud befure we
lave,' he says. 'I've listened to th' speeches
here to-night with satisfaction,' he says.
'I'm proud to see th' rayform wave have
sthruck th' road,' he says. 'Th' rascals
must be dhriven fr'm th' high places,' he
says. 'I see befure me in a chair a gintleman who wud steal a red-hot stove an'
freeze th' lid befure he got home. On me
right is th' gintleman who advanced th'
wave iv rayform tin years ago be puttin'
Mrs. Geohegan out on th' sthreet in a snow-
storm whin she was roarin' with a cough.
Mrs. Geohegan have rayformed, peace be
with her undher th' dhrifts iv Calv'ry! I
am greeted be th' smile iv me ol' frind
Higgins. We are ol' frinds, Dinnis, now,
ain't we? D'ye mind th' calls I made on
ye, with th' stamps undher me arms, whin I
wurruked in th' post-office? I've thought
iv thim whin th' lockstep was goin' in to
dinner, an' prayed f'r th' day whin I might

see ye again. An' you, Misther Brannigan,
who knows about vacant lots, an' you
Misther Clancy, th' frind iv th' dhrunk an'
disordherly, we're proud to have ye here.
'Tis be such as ye that th' polisman who
dhrinks on th' sly, an' th' saloon-keeper that
keeps open f'r th' la-ads an' th' newsboys
that shoots craps, 'll be brought to justice.
Down with crime! says I. Fellow-citizens,
I thank ye kindly. Th' meetin' is adjourned
siney dee; an' I app'int Missers Dooley,
O'Brien, Casey, Pug Slattery, an' mesilf to
lade out th' Lexow Sodality be th' nose.'"

Mr. McKenna arose sleepily, and walked
toward the door.

"Jawn," said Mr. Dooley.

"Yes," responded Mr. McKenna.

"Niver steal a dure-mat," said Mr.
Dooley. "If ye do, ye'll be invistigated,
hanged, an' maybe rayformed. Steal a bank,
me boy, steal a bank."

THEIR EXCELLENCIES, THE POLICE.

"Ye'll be goin' home early to-night, Jawn dear," said Mr. Dooley to Mr. McKenna.

"And for why?" said that gentleman, tilting lazily back in the chair.

"Because gin'ral ordher number wan is out," said Mr. Dooley, "directin' th' polis to stop ivry man catched out afther midnight an' make thim give a satisfacthry account iv thimsilves or run thim off to jail. Iv coorse, ye'll be pinched, f'r ye won't dare say where ye come fr'm; an' 'tis twinty-eight to wan, the odds again an Orangeman at a wake, that ye'll not know where ye're goin'."

"Tut, tut," said Mr. McKenna, indifferently.

"Ye may tut-tut till ye lay an egg," said Mr. Dooley, severely, "ye ol' hen; but 'tis so. I read it in th' pa-papers yesterdah afthernoon that Brinnan—'tis queer how thim Germans all get to be polismin, they're bright men, th' Germans, I don't think—

Brinnan says, says he, that th' city do be
overrun with burglars an' highwaymen, so
he ordhers th' polis to stick up ivry pedes-
threen they meet afther closin' time. 'Tis
good for him he named th' hour, f'r 'tis few
pedesthreens save an' except th' little kids
with panneckers that most iv th' polis meet
befure midnight.   Look at there table, will
ye? 'An ax done it,' says ye?   No, faith,
but th' fist iv a Kerry polisman they put on
this here bate last week.   He done it ladin'
thrumps. 'Thank Gawd,'' says I, 'ye didn't
have a good hand,' I says, 'or I might have
to call in th' wreckin' wagon.'   Thim Kerry
men shud be made to play forty-fives with
boxin'-gloves on.

" I read about th' ordher, but it slipped
me min' las' night.   I was down at a meetin'
iv th' Hugh O'Neills, an' a most intherestin'
meetin' it was, Jawn.   I'd been niglictful iv
me jooty to th' cause iv late, an' I was surprised an' shocked to hear how poor ol' Ireland was sufferin'.   Th' rayport fr'm th'
Twinty-third Wa-ard, which is in th' County

Mayo, showed that th' sthreet clanin' conthract had been give to a Swede be th' name
iv Oleson ; an' over in th' Nineteenth Wa-ard
th' County Watherford is all stirred up because Johnny Powers is filled th' pipe-ya-ard
with his own rilitives. I felt dam lonely,
an' with raison, too ; f'r I was th' on'y man
in th' camp that didn't have a job. An' says
I, 'Gintlemen,' says I, 'can't I do something f'r Ireland, too?' I says. 'I'd make a
gr-reat city threasurer,' says I, 'if ye've th'
job handy,' I says ; and at that they give me
th' laugh, and we tuk up a subscription an'
adjourned.

"Well, sir, I started up Ar-rchey Road
afther th' meetin', forgettin' about Brennan's
ordhers, whin a man jumps out fr'm behind
a tree near th' gas-house. 'Melia murther!'
says I to mesilf. ''Tis a highwayman!'
Thin, puttin' on a darin' front an' reachin'
f'r me handkerchief, I says, 'Stand back,
robber!' I says. 'Stand back, robber!' I
says. 'Stand back!' I says.

"'Excuse *me*,' says th' la-ad. 'I beg
ye'er pardon,' he says.

" ' Beg th' pardon iv Hiven,' says I, 'f'r stoppin' a desperate man in th' sthreet,' says I ; 'f'r in a holy minyit I'll blow off th' head iv ye,' says I, with me hand on th' handkerchief that niver blew nawthin' but this nose iv mine."

" ' I humbly ask your pardon,' he says, showin' a star ; ' but I'm a polisman.'

" ' Polisman or robber,' says I, ' stand aside !' I says.

" ' I'm a polisman,' he says, 'an' I'm undher ordhers to be polite with citizens I stop,' he says ; ' but, if ye don't duck up that road in half a minyit, ye poy-faced, red-eyed, lop-eared, thick-headed ol' bosthoon,' he says, ' I'll take ye be th' scruff iv th' neck an' thrun ye into th' ga-as-house tank,' he says, 'if I'm coort-martialed f'r it to-morrow.'

" Thin I knew he *was* a polisman ; an' I wint away, Jawn."

SHAUGHNESSY.

"JAWN," said Mr. Dooley in the course of the conversation, "whin ye come to think iv it, th' heroes iv th' wurruld,— an' be thim I mean th' lads that've buckled on th' gloves, an' gone out to do th' best they cud,— they ain't in it with th' quite people nayether you nor me hears tell iv fr'm wan end iv th' year to another."

"I believe it," said Mr. McKenna; "for my mother told me so."

"Sure," said Mr. Dooley, "I know it is an old story. Th' wurruld's been full iv it fr'm th' beginnin'; an' 'll be full iv it till, as Father Kelly says, th' pay-roll's closed. But I was thinkin' more iv it th' other night thin iver befure, whin I wint to see Shaughnessy marry off his on'y daughter. You know Shaughnessy,— a quite man that come into th' road befure th' fire. He wurruked f'r Larkin, th' conthractor, f'r near twinty years without skip or break, an' seen th' fam'ly grow up be candle-light.

Th' oldest boy was intinded f'r a priest. 'Tis a poor fam'ly that hasn't some wan that's bein' iddycated f'r the priesthood while all th' rest wear thimsilves to skeletons f'r him, an' call him Father Jawn 'r Father Mike whin he comes home wanst a year, light-hearted an' free, to eat with thim.

"Shaughnessy's lad wint wrong in his lungs, an' they fought death f'r him f'r five years, sindin' him out to th' Wist an' havin' masses said f'r him ; an', poor divvle, he kept comin' back cross an' crool, with th' fire in his cheeks, till wan day he laid down, an' says he : ' Pah,' he says, ' I'm goin' to give up,' he says. ' An' I on'y ask that ye'll have th' mass sung over me be some man besides Father Kelly,' he says. An' he wint, an' Shaughnessy come clumpin' down th' aisle like a man in a thrance.

"Well, th' nex' wan was a girl, an' she didn't die ; but, th' less said, th' sooner mended. Thin they was Terrence, a big, bould, curly-headed lad that cocked his hat at anny man,— or woman f'r th' matter iv that,— an' that bruk th' back iv a polisman an' swum to th' crib, an' was champeen iv th' South Side at hand ball. An' he wint. Thin th' good woman passed away. An' th' twins they growed to be th' prettiest pair that wint to first communion; an' wan night they was a light in th' window of Shaughnessy's house till three in th' mornin'. I raymimber it; f'r I had quite a crowd iv Willum Joyce's men in, an' we wondhered at it, an' wint home whin th' lamp in Shaughnessy's window was blown out.

"They was th' wan girl left,— Theresa, a big, clean-lookin' child that I see grow up fr'm hello to good avnin'. She thought on'y iv th' ol' man, an' he leaned on her as if she was a crutch. She was out to meet him in th' evnin'; an' in th' mornin' he, th' simple ol' man, 'd stop to blow a kiss at her an' wave his dinner-pail, lookin' up an' down th' r-road to see that no wan was watchin' him.

"I dinnaw what possessed th' young Donahue, fr'm th' Nineteenth. I niver thought much iv him, a stuck-up, aisy-come la-ad that niver had annything but a civil wurrud, an' is prisident iv th' sodality. But he came in, an' married Theresa Shaughnessy las' Thursdah night. Th' ol' man took on twinty years, but he was as brave as a gin'ral iv th' army. He cracked jokes an' he made speeches; an' he took th' pipes fr'm under th' elbow iv Hogan, th' blindman, an' played 'Th' Wind that shakes th' Barley' till ye'd have wore ye'er leg to a smoke f'r wantin' to dance. Thin he wint to th' dure with th' two iv thim; an' says he, 'Well,' he says, 'Jim, be good to her,' he says, an' shook hands with her through th' carredge window.

"Him an' me sat a long time smokin' across th' stove. Fin'lly, says I, 'Well,' I says, 'I must be movin'.' 'What's th' hurry?' says he. 'I've got to go,' says I. 'Wait a moment,' says he. 'Theresa 'll'— He stopped right there f'r a minyit, holdin' to th' back iv th' chair. 'Well,' says he, 'if ye've got to go, ye must,' he says. 'I'll

show ye out,' he says. An' he come with
me to th' dure, holdin' th' lamp over his
head. I looked back at him as I wint by;
an' he was settin' be th' stove, with his
elbows on his knees an' th' empty pipe
between his teeth."

TIMES PAST.

Mr. McKenna, looking very warm and tired, came in to Mr. Dooley's tavern one night last week, and smote the bar with his fist.

"What's the matter with Hogan?" he said.

"What Hogan?" asked Mr. Dooley. "Malachy or Matt? Dinnis or Mike? Sarsfield or William Hogan? There's a Hogan f'r ivry block in th' Ar-rchey Road, an' wan to spare. There's nawthin' th' matter with anny iv thim; but, if ye mean Hogan, th' liquor dealer, that r-run f'r aldherman, I'll say to ye he's all right. Mind ye, Jawn, I'm doin' this because ye're me frind; but, by gar, if anny wan else comes in an' asks me that question, I'll kill him, if I have to go to th' bridewell f'r it. I'm no health officer."

Having delivered himself of this tirade, Mr. Dooley scrutinized Mr. McKenna sharply, and continued: "Ye've been out

ilictin' some man, Jawn, an' ye needn't deny
it. I seen it th' minyit ye come in. Ye'er
hat's dinted, an' ye have ye'er necktie over
ye'er ear; an' I see be ye'er hand ye've hit
a Dutchman. Jawn, ye know no more about
politics thin a mimber iv this here Civic Featheration. Didn't ye have a beer bottle or an
ice-pick? Ayether iv thim is good, though,
whin I was a young man an' precint captain
an' intherested in th' welfare iv th' counthry,
I found a couplin' pin in a stockin' about as
handy as annything.

"Thim days is over, though, Jawn, an'
between us politics don't intherest me no
more. They ain't no liveliness in thim.
Whin Andy Duggan r-run f'r aldherman
against Schwartzmeister, th' big Dutchman,
— I was precinct captain then, Jawn,— there
was an iliction f'r ye. 'Twas on our precinct
they relied to ilict Duggan; f'r the Dutch
was sthrong down be th' thrack, an' Schwartzmeister had a band out playin' 'Th' Watch
on th' Rhine.' Well, sir, we opened th'
polls at six o'clock, an' there was tin Schwartz-

meister men there to protect his intherests.
At sivin o'clock there was only three, an'
wan iv thim was goin' up th' sthreet with
Hinnissy kickin' at him. At eight o'clock,
be dad,'there was on'y wan; an' he was sittin'
on th' roof iv Gavin's blacksmith shop, an'
th' la-ads was thryin' to borrow a laddher
fr'm th' injine-house f'r to get at him.
'Twas thruck eighteen; an' Hogan, that was
captain, wudden't let thim have it. Not ye'er
Hogan, Jawn, but th' meanest fireman in
Bridgeport. He got kilt aftherwards. He
wudden't let th' la-ads have a laddher, an' th'
Dutchman stayed up there; an', whin there
was nawthin' to do, we wint over an' thrun
bricks at him. 'Twas gr-reat sport.

"About four in th' afthernoon Schwartzmeister's band come up Ar-rchey Road,
playin' 'Th' Watch on th' Rhine.' Whin
it got near Gavin's, big Peter Nolan tuk a
runnin' jump, an' landed feet first in th' big
bass dhrum. Th' man with th' dhrum walloped him over th' head with th' dhrum-
stick, an' Dorsey Quinn wint over an' tuk

a slide trombone away fr'm the musician an'
clubbed th' bass dhrum man with it. Thin
we all wint over, an' ye niver see th' like in
ye'er born days. Th' las' I see iv th' band
it was goin' down th' road towards th'
slough with a mob behind it, an' all th' polis
foorce fr'm Deerin' Sthreet afther th' mob.
Th' la-ads collected th' horns an th' dhrums,
an' that started th' Ar-rchey Road brass
band. Little Mike Doyle larned to play
'Th' Rambler fr'm Clare' beautifully on
what they call a pickle-e-o befure they sarved
a rayplivin writ on him.

"We cast twinty-wan hundherd votes f'r
Duggan, an' they was on'y five hundherd
votes in th' precinct. We'd cast more, but
th' tickets give out. They was tin votes in
th' box f'r Schwartzmeister whin we counted
up; an' I felt that mortified I near died, me
bein' precinct captain, an' res-sponsible.
'What 'll we do with thim? Out th' window,'
says I. Just thin Dorsey's nanny-goat that
died next year put her head through th'
dure. 'Monica,' says Dorsey (he had pretty

names for all his goats), 'Monica, are ye
hungry,' he says, 'ye poor dear?' Th'
goat give him a pleadin' look out iv her big
brown eyes. 'Can't I make ye up a nice
supper?' says Dorsey. 'Do ye like paper?'
he says. 'Would ye like to help desthroy a
Dutchman,' he says, 'an' perform a sarvice
f'r ye'er counthry?' he says. Thin he wint
out in th' next room, an' come back with a
bottle iv catsup; an' he poured it on th'
Schwartzmeister ballots, an' Monica et thim
without winkin'.

"Well, sir, we ilicted Duggan; an' what
come iv it? Th' week befure iliction he
was in me house ivry night, an' 'twas
'Misther Dooley, this,' an' 'Mr. Dooley,
that,' an' 'What 'll ye have, boys?' an'
'Niver mind about th' change.' I niver see
hide nor hair iv him f'r a week afther iliction. Thin he come with a plug hat on, an'
says he: 'Dooley,' he says, 'give me a shell
iv beer,' he says: 'give me a shell iv beer,'
he says, layin' down a nickel. 'I suppose
ye're on th' sub-scription,' he says. 'What

for?' says I. 'F'r to buy me a goold star,'
says he. With that I eyes him, an' says I :
'Duggan,' I says, 'I knowed ye whin ye
didn't have a coat to ye'er back,' I says, 'an'
I'll buy no star f'r ye,' I says. 'But I'll
tell ye what I'll buy f'r ye,' I says. 'I'll buy
rayqueem masses f'r th' raypose iv ye'er
sowl, if ye don't duck out iv this in a minyit.' Whin I seen him last, he was back
dhrivin' a dhray an' atin' his dinner out iv a
tin can."

THE SKIRTS OF CHANCE.

THE people of Bridgeport are not solicitous of modern improvements, and Mr. Dooley views with distaste the new and garish. But he consented to install a nickel-in-the-slot machine in his tavern last week, and it was standing on a table when Mr. McKenna came in. It was a machine that looked like a house; and, when you put a nickel in at the top of it, either the door opened and released three other nickels or it did not. Mostly it did not.

Mr. Dooley saluted Mr. McKenna with unusual cordiality, and Mr. McKenna inspected the nickel-in-the-slot machine with affectation of much curiosity.

"What's this you have here, at all?" said Mr. McKenna.

"'Tis an aisy way iv gettin' rich," said Mr. Dooley. "All ye have to do is to dhrop a nickel in th' slot, an' three other nickels come out at th' dure. Ye can play it all afthernoon, an' take a fortune fr'm it if ye'er nickels hould out."

"And where do th' nickels come fr'm?" asked Mr. McKenna.

"I put thim in," said Mr. Dooley. "Ivry twenty minutes I feed th' masheen a hatful iv nickels, so that whin me frinds dhrop in they won't be dissypinted, d'ye mind. 'Tis a fine invistment for a young man. Little work an' large profits. It rayminds me iv Hogan's big kid an' what he done with his coin. He made a lot iv it in dhrivin' a ca-ar, he did, but he blew it all in again good liquor an' bad women; an', bedad, he was broke half th' time an' borrowin' th' other half. So Hogan gets in Father Kelly fr'm up west iv th' bridge, an' they set in with Dinnis to talk him out iv his spind-thrift ways. 'I have plenty to keep mesilf,' says Hogan, he says. 'But,' he says, 'I want ye to save ye'er money,' he says, 'f'r a rainy day.' 'He's right, Dinnis,' says th' soggarth,— 'he's right,' he says. 'Ye should save a little in case ye need it,' he says. 'Why don't ye take two dollars,' says th' priest, 'an' invist it ivry month,' says he, 'in somethin',' says he, 'that'll give ye profits,' says he. 'I'll do it,' says Dinnis,— 'I'll do it,' he says. Well, sir, Hogan was that tickled he give th' good man five bones out iv th' taypot; but, faith, Dinnis was back at his reg'lar game before th' week was out, an', after a month or two, whin Hogan had to get th' tayspoons out iv soak, he says to th' kid, he says, 'I thought ye was goin' to brace up,' he says, 'an' here ye're burnin' up ye'er money,' he says. 'Didn't ye promise to invist two dollars ivry month?' he says. 'I'm doin' it,' says Dinnis. 'I've kept me wurrud.' 'An' what are ye invistin' it in?' says Hogan. 'In lotthry tickets,' says th' imp'dent kid.''

While delivering these remarks, Mr. Dooley was peeping over his glasses at Mr. McKenna, who was engaged in a struggle with the machine. He dropped a nickel and it rattled down the slot, but it did not open the door.

"Doesn't it open?" said Mr. Dooley.

"It does not."

"Shake it thin," said Mr. Dooley. "Something must be wrong."

Mr. McKenna shook the machine when he inserted the next nickel, but there was no compensatory flow of coins from the door.

"Perhaps the money is bad," suggested Mr. Dooley. "It won't open f'r bad money."

Thereupon he returned to his newspaper, observing which Mr. McKenna drew from his pocket a nickel attached to a piece of string and dropped it into the slot repeatedly. After a while the door popped open, and Mr. McKenna thrust in his hand expectantly. There was no response, and he turned in great anger to Mr. Dooley.

"There ain't any money there," he said.

"Ye're right, Jawn," responded Mr. Dooley. "If ye expect to dhraw anny coin fr'm that there masheen, ye may call on some iv ye'er rough frinds down town f'r a brace an' bit an' a jimmy. Jawn, me la-ad, I see th' nickel with th' string befure; an', to provide again it, I improved th' masheen. Thim nickels ye dhropped in are all in th' dhrawer iv that there table, an' to-morrow mornin' ye may see me havin' me hair cut be means iv thim. An' I'll tell ye wan thing, Jawn McKenna, an' that's not two things, that if ye think ye can come up here to Ar-rchey Road an' rob an honest man, by gar, ye've made th' mistake iv ye'er life. Goowan, now, befure I call a polisman."

Mr. McKenna stopped at the door only long enough to shake his fist at the proprietor, who responded with a grin of pure contentment.

WHEN THE TRUST IS AT WORK.

" WHICH d'ye think makes th' best fun'ral
turnout, th' A-ho-aitches or th' Saint Vincent de Pauls, Jawn? " asked Mr. Dooley.

" I don't know," said Mr. McKenna.
" Are you thinking of leaving us? "

" Faith, I am not," said Mr. Dooley.
" Since th' warm weather's come an' th'
wind's in th' south, so that I can tell at
night that A-armoor an' me ol' frind, Jawn
Brinnock, are attindin' to business, I have a
grip on life like th' wan ye have on th'
shank iv that shell iv malt. Whether 'tis
these soft days, with th' childher beginnin'
to play barefutted in th' sthreet an' th' good
women out to palaver over th' fence without
their shawls, or whether 'tis th' wan wurrud
Easter Sundah that comes on me, an' jolts
me up with th' thoughts iv th' la-ads goin'
to mass an' th' blackthorn turnin' green
beyant, I dinnaw. But annyhow I'm as gay
as a babby an' as fresh as a lark. I am so.

" I was on'y thinkin'. Ol' Gran'pah

Grogan died las' Mondah,— as good a man
as e'er counted his beads or passed th' plate.
A thrue man. Choosdah a Connock man
up back iv th' dumps laid down th' shovel.
Misther Grogan had a grand notice in th'
pa-apers : 'Grogan, at his late risidence, 279
A-archoor Avnoo, Timothy Alexander, beloved husband iv th' late Mary Grogan,
father iv Maurice, Michael, Timothy, Ed-
ward, James, Peter, Paul, an' Officer Andrew
Grogan, iv Cologne Sthreet station, an' iv
Mrs. Willum Sarsfield Cassidy, nee Grogan'
(which manes that was her name befure she
marrid Cassidy, who wurruks down be
Haley's packin'-house). 'Fun'ral be car-
riages fr'm his late risidence to Calv'ry cim-
ithry. Virginia City, Nivada ; St. Joseph,
Mitchigan ; an' Clonmel Tipp'rary pa-apers
please copy.'

"I didn't see e'er a nee about th' fam'ly
iv th' little man back iv th' dumps, though
maybe he had wan to set aroun' th' fire in
th' dark an' start at th' tap iv a heel on th'
dure-step. Mebbe he had a fam'ly, poor

things. A fun'ral is great la-arks f'r th'
neighbors, an' 'tis not so bad f'r th' corpse.
But in these times, Jawn dear, a-ho th' gray
hearts left behind an' th' hungry mouths to
feed. They done th' best they cud f'r th'
Connock man back iv th' dumps,— give him
all th' honors, th' A-ho-aitches ma-archin'
behind th' hearse an' th' band playin' th'
Dead March. 'Twas almost as good a
turnout as Grogan had, though th' Saint
Vincents had betther hats an' looked more
like their fam'lies kept a cow.

"But they was two hacks back iv th'
pall-bearers. I wondhered what was passin'
behind th' faces I seen again their windys.
'Twas well f'r himself, too. Little odds to
him, afther th' last screw was twisted be
Gavin's ol' yellow hands, whether beef was
wan cint or a hundherd dollars th' pound.
But there's comin' home as well as goin' out.
There's more to a fun'ral thin th' lucks par-
pitua, an' th' clod iv sullen earth on th' top
iv th' crate. Sare a pax vobiscum is there
f'r thim that's huddled in th' ol' hack,

sthragglin' home in th' dust to th' empty panthry an' th' fireless grate.

"Mind ye, Jawn, I've no wurrud to say again thim that sets back in their own house an' lot an' makes th' food iv th' people dear. They're good men, good men. Whin they tilt th' price iv beef to where wan pound iv it costs as much as manny th' man in this Ar-rchey Road 'd wurruk fr'm th' risin' to th' settin' iv th' sun to get, they have no thought iv th' likes iv you an' me. 'Tis aisy come, aisy go with thim; an' ivry cint a pound manes a new art musoom or a new church, to take th' edge off hunger. They're all right, thim la-ads, with their own pork-chops delivered free at th' door. 'Tis, ' Will ye have a new spring dhress, me dear? Willum, ring thim up, an' tell thim to hist th' price iv beef. If we had a few more pitchers an' statoos in th' musoom, 'twud ilivate th' people a sthory or two. Willum, afther this steak 'll be twinty cints a pound.' Oh, they're all right, on'y I was thinkin' iv th' Connock man's fam'ly back iv th' dumps."

"For a man that was gay a little while ago, it looks to me as if you'd grown mighty solemn-like," said Mr. McKenna.

"Mebbe so," said Mr. Dooley. "Mebbe so. What th' 'ell, annyhow. Mebbe 'tis as bad to take champagne out iv wan man's mouth as round steak out iv another's. Lent is near over. I seen Doherty out shinin' up his pipe that's been behind th' clock since Ash Winsdah. Th' girls 'll be layin' lilies on th' altar in a day or two. Th' spring's come on. Th' grass is growin' good; an', if th' Connock man's children back iv th' dumps can't get meat, they can eat hay."

A BRAND FROM THE BURNING.

"I see be th' pa-apers," said Mr. Dooley, "that Boss have flew th' coop. 'Tis too bad, too bad. He wa-as a gr-reat man."

"Is he dead?" asked Mr. McKenna.

"No, faith, worse thin that; he's resigned. He calls th' la-ads about him, an' says he: 'Boys,' he says, 'I'm tired iv politics,' he says. 'I'm goin' to quit it f'r me health,' he says. 'Do ye stay in, an' get ar-rested f'r th' good iv th' party.' Ye see thim mugwumps is afther th' Boss, an' he's gettin' out th' way Hogan got out iv Connock. Wan day he comes over to me fa-ather's house, an' says he, 'Dooley,' he says, 'I'm goin' to lave this hole iv a place,' he says. 'F'r why?' says th' ol' man; 'I thought ye liked it.' 'Faith,' says Hogan, 'I niver liked a blade iv grass in it,' he says. 'I'm sick iv it,' he says. 'I don't want niver to see it no more.' And he wint away. Th' next mornin' th' polis was lookin' f'r him to lock him up f'r stealin' joo'lry in the fair town. Yes, by dad.

" 'Tis th' way iv th' boss, Jawn. I seen
it manny's th' time. There was wanst a
boss in th' Sixth Wa-ard, an' his name was
Flannagan; an' he came fr'm th' County
Clare, but so near th' bordher line that no
wan challenged his vote, an' he was let walk
down Ar-rchey Road just 's though he come
fr'm Connock. Well, sir, whin I see him
first, he'd th' smell iv Castle Garden on him,
an' th' same is no mignonette, d'ye mind;
an' he was goin' out with pick an' shovel f'r
to dig in th' canal,— a big, shtrappin', black-
haired lad, with a neck like a bull's an' covered with a hide as thick as wan's, fr'm
thryin' to get a crop iv oats out iv a Clare
farm that growed divvle th' thing but nice,
big boldhers.

" He was de-termined, though, an' th'
first man that made a face at him he walloped in th' jaw; an' he'd been on th' canal
no more thin a month befure he licked ivry
man in th' gang but th' section boss, who'd
been a Dublin jackeen, an' weighed sixteen
stone an' was great with a thrip an' a punch.

Wan day they had some wurruds, whin me
bold Dublin man sails into Flannagan.
Well, sir, they fought fr'm wan o'clock till
tin in th' night, an' nayther give up; though
Flannagan had th' best iv it, bein' young.
'Why don't ye put him out?' says wan iv
th' la-ads. 'Whisht,' says Flannagan. 'I'm
waitin' f'r th' moon to come up,' he says,
'so's I can hit him right,' he says, 'an' sci-
entific.' Well, sir, his tone was that fierce
th' section boss he dhropped right there iv
sheer fright; an' Flannagan was cock iv th'
walk.

"Afther a while he begun f'r to go out
among th' other gangs, lookin' f'r fight; an',
whin th' year was over, he was knowed fr'm
wan end iv th' canal to th' other as th' man
that no wan cud stand befure. He got so
pop'lar fr'm lickin' all his frinds that he
opened up a liquor store beyant th' bridge,
an' wan night he shot some la-ads fr'm th'
ya-ards that come over f'r to r-run him.
That made him sthronger still. When they
got up a prize f'r th' most pop'lar man

in th' parish, he loaded th' ballot box an'
got th' goold-headed stick, though he was
r-runnin' against th' aldherman, an' th' little
soggarth thried his best to down him.   Thin
he give a cock fight in th' liquor shop, an'
that atthracted a gang iv bad men ; an' he
licked thim wan afther another, an' made
thim his frinds.   An' wan day lo an' behold,
whin th' aldherman thried f'r to carry th'
prim'ries that'd niver failed him befure,
Flannagan wint down with his gang an'
illicted his own dilligate ticket, an' thrun th'
aldherman up in th' air !

  " Thin he was a boss, an' f'r five years he
r-run th' ward.   He niver wint to th' council, d'ye mind ; but, whin he was gin'rous, he
give th' aldhermen tin per cint iv what they
made.   In a convintion, whin anny iv th'
candydates passed roun' th' money, 'twas
wan thousand dollars f'r Flannagan an' have
a nice see-gar with me f'r th' rest iv thim.
Wan year fr'm th' day he done th' aldherman he sold th' liquor shop.   Thin he built
a brick house in th' place iv th' little frame

wan he had befure, an' moved in a pianny
f'r his daughter.   'Twas about this time he
got a dimon as big as ye'er fist, an' begun to
dhrive down town behind a fast horse.   No
wan knowed what he done, but his wife said
he was in th' r-rale estate business.   D'ye
mind, Jawn, that th' r-rale estate business
includes near ivrything fr'm vagrancy to
manslaughter?

" Whativer it was he done, he had money
to bur-rn; an' th' little soggarth that wanst
despised him, but had a hard time payin' th'
debt iv th' church, was glad enough to sit at
his table.   Wan day without th' wink iv th'
eye he moved up in th' avnoo, an' no wan
seen him in Bridgeport afther that.   'Twas a
month or two later whin a lot iv th' la-ads
was thrun into jail f'r a little diviltry they'd
done f'r him.   A comity iv th' fathers iv
th' la-ads wint to see him.   He raceived thim
in a room as big as wan iv their whole
houses, with pitchers on th' walls an' a car-
pet as deep an' soft as a bog.   Th' comity
asked him to get th' la-ads out on bail.

"'Gintlemen,' he says, 'ye must excuse me,' he says, 'in such matthers.' 'D'ye mane to say,' says Cassidy, th' plumber, 'that ye won't do annything f'r my son?' 'Do annything,' says Flannagan. (I'll say this f'r him: a more darin' man niver drew breath; an', whin his time come to go sthandin' off th' mob an' defindin' his sthone quarry in th' rites iv sivinty-siven, he faced death without a wink.) 'Do?' he says, risin' an' sthandin' within a fut iv Cassidy's big cane. 'Do?' he says. 'Why,' he says, 'yes,' he says; 'I've subscribed wan thousand dollars,' he says, 'to th' citizen's comity,' he says, 'f'r to prosecute him; an',' he says, 'gintlemen,' he says, 'there's th' dure.'

"I seen Cassidy that night, an' he was as white as a ghost. 'What ails ye?' says I. 'Have ye seen th' divvle?' 'Yes,' he says, bendin' his head over th' bar, an' lookin' sivinty years instead iv forty-five."

A WINTER NIGHT.

ANY of the Archey Road cars that got out of the barns at all were pulled by teams of four horses, and the snow hung over the shoulders of the drivers' big bearskin coats like the eaves of an old-fashioned house on the blizzard night. There was hardly a soul in the road from the red bridge, west, when Mr. McKenna got laboriously off the platform of his car and made for the sign of somebody's celebrated Milwaukee beer over Mr. Dooley's tavern. Mr. Dooley, being a man of sentiment, arranges his drinks to conform with the weather. Now anybody who knows anything at all knows that a drop of " J. J." and a whisper (subdued) of hot water and a lump of sugar and lemon peel (if you care for lemon peel) and nutmeg (if you are a "jood") is a drink calculated to tune a man's heart to the song of the wind slapping a beer-sign upside down and the snow drifting in under the door. Mr. Dooley was drinking this mixture be-

hind his big stove when Mr. McKenna
came in.

"Bad night, Jawn," said Mr. Dooley.

"It is that," said Mr. McKenna.

"Blowin' an' stormin', yes," said Mr.
Dooley. "There hasn' been a can in to-
night but wan, an' that was a pop bottle.
Is the snow-ploughs out, I dinnaw?"

"They are," said Mr. McKenna.

"I suppose Doherty is dhrivin'," said
Mr. Dooley. "He's a good dhriver. They
do say he do be wan iv the best dhrivers on
th' road. I've heerd that th' prisident is
dead gawn on him. He's me cousin. Ye
can't tell much about what a man 'll be fr'm
what th' kid is. That there Doherty was
th' worst omadhon iv a boy that iver I
knowed. He niver cud larn his a-ah-bee,
abs. But see what he made iv himsilf!
Th' best dhriver on th' road; an', by dad,
'tis not twinty to wan he won't be stharter
befure he dies. 'Tis in th' fam'ly to make
their names. There niver was anny fam'ly
in th' ol' counthry that turned out more

priests than th' Dooleys. By gar, I believe
we hol' th' champeenship iv th' wurruld.
At M'nooth th' profissor that called th' roll
got so fr'm namin' th' Dooley la-ads that
he came near bein' tur-rned down on th'
cha-arge that he was whistlin' at vespers.
His mouth, d'ye mind, took that there
shape fr'm sayin' ' Dooley,' ' Dooley,' that
he'd looked as if he was whistlin'. D'ye
mind? Dear, oh dear, 'tis th' divvle's own
fam'ly f'r religion."

Mr. McKenna was about to make a jeer-
ing remark to the effect that the alleged
piety of the Dooley family had not pene-
trated to the Archey Road representative,
when a person, evidently of wayfaring habits,
entered and asked for alms. Mr. Dooley
arose, and, picking a half-dollar from the
till, handed it to the visitor with great un-
concern. The departure of the wayfarer
with profuse thanks was followed by a space
of silence.

"Well, Jawn," said Mr. Dooley.

"What did you give the hobo?" asked
Mr. McKenna.

" Half a dollar," said Mr. Dooley.

" And what for ? "

" Binivolence," said Mr. Dooley, with a seraphic smile.

" Well," said Mr. McKenna, " I should say that was benevolence."

" Well," said Mr. Dooley, " 'tis a bad night out, an' th' poor divvle looked that mis'rable it brought th' tears to me eyes, an' " —

" But," said Mr. McKenna, " that ain't any reason why you should give half a dollar to every tramp who comes in."

" Jawn," said Mr. Dooley, " I know th' ma-an. He spinds all his money at Schneider's, down th' block."

" What of that ? " asked Mr. McKenna.

" Oh, nawthin'," said Mr. Dooley, " on'y I hope Herman won't thry to bite that there coin. If he does " —

THE BLUE AND THE GRAY.

"A-ho," said Mr. Dooley, "th' blue an' th' gray, th' blue an' th' gray. Well, sir, Jawn, d'ye know that I see Mulligan marchin' ahead with his soord on his side, an' his horse dancin' an' backin' into th' crowd; an' th' la-ads chowlder arms an' march, march away. Ye shud 've been there. Th' women come down fr'm th' peeraries with th' childher in their arms, an' 'twas like a sind-off to a picnic. 'Good-by, Mike.' 'Timothy, darlin', don't forget your prayers.' 'Cornalius, if ye do but look out f'r th' little wans, th' big wans 'll not harm ye.' 'Teddy, lad, always wear ye'er Agnus Day.' An', whin th' time come f'r th' thrain to lave, th' girls was up to th' lines; an' 'twas, 'Mike, love, ye'll come back alive, won't ye?' an' 'Pat, there does be a pair iv yarn socks in th' hoomp on ye'er back. Wear thim, lad. They'll be good f'r ye'er poor, dear feet.' An' off they wint.

"Well, some come back, an' some did

not come back. An' some come back with
no rale feet f'r to put yarn socks on thim.
Mulligan quit down somewhere in Ken-
tucky; an' th' las' wurruds he was heard to
utter was, 'Lay me down, boys, an' save
th' flag.' An there was manny th' other
that had nawthin' to say but to call f'r a
docthor; f'r 'tis on'y, d'ye mind, th' heroes
that has somethin' writ down on typewriter
f'r to sind to th' newspapers whin they move
up. Th' other lads that dies because they
cudden't r-run away,— not because they wudden't,— they dies on their backs, an' calls f'r
th' docthor or th' priest. It depinds where
they're shot.

"But, annyhow, no wan iv thim lads
come back to holler because he was in th'
war or to war again th' men that shot him.
They wint to wurruk, carryin' th' hod 'r
shovellin' cindhers at th' rollin' mills. Some
iv thim took pinsions because they needed
thim; but divvle th' wan iv thim ye'll see
paradin' up an' down Ar-rchey Road with
a blue coat on, wantin' to fight th' war over

with Schwartzmeister's bar-tinder that niver
heerd iv but wan war, an' that th' rites
iv sivinty-sivin. Sare a wan. No, faith.
They'd as lave decorate a confeatherate's
grave as a thrue pathrite's. All they want
is a chanst to go out to th' cimitry ; an', faith,
who doesn't enjoy that? No wan that's
annything iv a spoort.

"I know hundhreds iv thim. Ye know
Pat Doherty, th' little man that lives over
be Grove Sthreet. He inlisted three times,
by dad, an' had to stand on his toes three
times to pass. He was that ager. Well,
he looks to weigh about wan hundherd an'
twinty pounds ; an' he weighs wan fifty be
raison iv him havin' enough lead to stock
a plumber in his stomach an' his legs. He
showed himsilf wanst whin he was feelin'
gay. He looks like a sponge. But he ain't.
He come in here Thursdah night to take
his dhrink in quite ; an' says I, 'Did ye
march to-day?' 'Faith, no,' he says, 'I
can get hot enough runnin' a wheelbarrow
without makin' a monkey iv mesilf dancin'

around th' sthreets behind a band.' 'But
didn't ye go out to decorate th' graves?'
says I. 'I hadn't th' price,' says he, 'Th'
women wint out with a gyranium to put
over Sarsfield, the first born,' he says.

"Just thin Morgan O'Toole come in, an'
laned over th' ba-ar. He's been a dillygate
to ivry town convention iv th' Raypublicans
since I dinnaw whin. 'Well,' says he, 'I
see they're pilin' it on,' he says. 'On th'
dead?' says I, be way iv a joke. 'No,' he
says; 'but did ye see they're puttin' up
a monnymint over th' rebils out here be
Oakwoods?' he says. 'By gar,' he says,
''tis a disgrace to th' mim'ries iv thim devoted dead who died f'r their counthry,' he
says. 'If,' he says, 'I cud get ninety-nine
men to go out an' blow it up, I'd be th'
hundherth,' he says. 'Yes,' says I, 'ye
wud,' I says. 'Ye'd be th' last,' I says.

"Doherty was movin' up to him. 'What
rig'ment?' says he. 'What's that?' says
O'Toole. 'Did ye inlist in th' army, brave
man?' says Pat. 'I swore him over age,' says

I. 'Was ye dhrafted in?' says th' little man.
'No,' says O'Toole. 'Him an' me was in
th' same cellar,' says I. 'Did ye iver hear
iv Ree-saca, 'r Vicksburg, 'r Lookout Moun-
tain?' th' little man wint on. 'Did anny
man iver shoot at ye with annything but a
siltzer bottle? Did ye iver have to lay on
ye'er stummick with ye'er nose burrid in th'
Lord knows what while things was whistlin'
over ye that, if they iver stopped whistlin', 'd
make ye'er backbone look like a broom?
Did ye iver see a man that ye'd slept with
th' night befure cough, an' go out with his
hands ahead iv his face? Did ye iver have
to wipe ye'er most intimate frinds off ye'er
clothes, whin ye wint home at night? Where
was he durin' th' war?' he says. 'He was
dhrivin' a grocery wagon f'r Philip Reidy,'
says I. 'An' what's he makin' th' roar
about?' says th' little man. 'He don't want
anny wan to get onto him,' says I.

"O'Toole was gone be this time, an' th'
little man laned over th' bar. 'Now,' says
he, 'what d'ye think iv a gazabo that don't

want a monniment put over some wan?
Where is this here pole? I think I'll go
out an' take a look at it. Where'd ye say
th' la-ad come fr'm? Donaldson? I was
there. There was a man in our mess — a
Wicklow man be th' name iv Dwyer — that
had th' best come-all-ye I iver heerd. It
wint like this,' an' he give it to me."

THE TRAGEDY OF THE
AGITATOR.

" Whin ye come up, did ye see Dorgan ? "
asked Mr. Dooley.

" Which Dorgan ? " asked Mr. McKenna.

" Why, to be sure, Hugh O'Neill Dorgan, him that was sicrety iv Deerin' Shtreet
branch number wan hundred an' eight iv th'
Ancient Ordher iv Scow Unloaders, him
that has th' red lambrequin on his throat,
that married th' second time to Dinnihy's
aunt an' we give a shivaree to him. Hivins
on earth, don't ye know him ? "

" I don't," said Mr. McKenna ; " and, if I
know him, I haven't seen him."

" Thin ye missed a sight," said Mr.
Dooley. " He's ragin' an' tearin'. He
have been a great union man. He'd sthrike
on th' moment's provocation. I seen him
wanst, whin some scow unloaders sthruck in
Lemont or some other distant place, put on
his coat, lay down his shovel, an' go out, be
hivins, alone. Well, his son goes an' jines

th' Sivinth Rig'mint; an', by gar, th' ol' man,
not knowin' about th' army, he's that proud
that he sthruts up an' down th' sthreet with
his thumb in th' vest iv him an' give his son
a new shovel, for they was wurrukin' together on th' scow 'Odelia Ann.' Well,
whin th' sthrike come along, iv coorse th'
scow unloaders quits; an' Dorgan an' th'
la-ad goes out together, because they're
dhrawin' good wages an' th' crick do be full
iv men r-ready f'r to take their places.

"Well, Dorgan had th' divvle's own time
paradin' up an' down an' sindin' out ordhers
to sthrike to ivry man he knowed of till th'
la-ad comes over las' Choosdah avenin',
dhressed in his rigimintals with a gun as
long as a clothes-pole over his shoulder.
'Hughey,' said th' father, 'you look very
gran' to-night,' he says. 'Whose fun'ral
ar-re ye goin' to at this hour?' 'None but
thim I makes mesilf,' says he. 'What d'ye
mean?' says th' ol' man. 'I'm goin' over
f'r to stand guard in th' thracks,' says th'
la-ad. Well, with that th' ol' man leaps up.

' Polisman,' he says. ' Polisman,' he says. ' Copper,' he says. 'Twas on'y be Mrs. Dorgan comin' in an' quitein' th' ol' man with a chair that hostilities was averted — as th' pa-apers says — right there an' thin.

" Well, sir, will ye believe me, whin Dorgan wint over with th' mimbers iv' th' union that night f'r to bur-rn something, there was me brave Hughey thrampin' up an' down like a polisman on bate.   Dorgan goes up an' shakes his fist at him, an' th' la-ad gives him a jab with his bayonet that makes th' poor ol' man roar like a bull. ' In th' name iv th' people iv th' State iv Illinys,' he says, ' disperse,' he says, ' ye riter,' he says ; ' an', if ye don't go home,' he says, ' ye ol' omadhon,' he says, ' I'll have ye thrun into jail,' he says.

" Dorgan   haven't   got   over   it   yet.   It dhruv him to a sick-bed."

BOYNE WATER AND BAD BLOOD.

"Jawn," said Mr. Dooley to Mr. McKenna, "what did th' Orangeys do to-day?"

"They had a procession," said Mr. McKenna.

"Was it much, I dinnaw?"

"Not much."

"That's good," said Mr. Dooley. "That's good. They don't seem to be gettin' anny sthronger, praise be! Divvle th' sthraw do I care f'r thim. They niver harmed hair nor head iv me; an' they ain't likely to, ayether, so long as th' R-road keeps th' way it is. Faith, 'twud be a fine pot iv porridge th' like iv thim 'd ate if they come up into Ar-rchey Road. I'm an ol' man, Jawn,— though not so ol' at that,— but I'd give tin years iv me life to see an Orange procession west on Ar-rchey Road with th' right flank restin' on Halsthed Sthreet. It'd rest there. Th' Lord knows it wud.

"Jawn, I have no dislike to th' Orangeys.

Nawthin' again thim. I'd not raise me
hand to thim, I wud not, though me cousin
Tim was kilt be wan iv thim dhroppin' a
bolt on his skull in th' ship-yards in Belfast.
'Twas lucky f'r that there Orangey he spoke
first. Me cousin Tim had a ship-ax in his
hand that'd 've evened things up f'r at laste
wan iv th' poor pikemen that Sarsfield had
along with him. But I've nawthin' again
thim at that but th' wan that kilt Tim. I'd
like to meet that lad in some quite place like
th' Clan-na-Gael picnic on th' fifteenth iv
August, some place where we'd have fair
play.

"Jawn, live an' let live is me motto.
On'y I say this here, that 'tis a black disgrace to Chicago f'r to let th' likes iv thim
thrapze about th' sthreets with their cheap
ol' flags an' ribbons. Oh dear, oh dear, if
Pathrick's Day on'y come some year on' th'
twelfth day iv July! Where'd they be,
where'd they be?

"D'ye know things is goin' to th' dogs in
this town, Jawn, avick? Sure they are, faith.

I mind th' time well whin an Orangey'd as lave go through hell in a celluloid suit as march in this here town on the twelfth iv July. I raymimber wanst they was a man be th' name iv Morgan Dempsey,— a first cousin iv thim Dempseys that lives in Cologne Sthreet,— an' he was a Roscommon man, too, an' wan iv th' cutest divvles that iver breathed th' breath iv life.

" Well, whin th' day come f'r th' Orangeys to cillybrate th' time whin King Willum — may th' divvle hould him ! — got a stand-off, — an' 'twas no bedther, Jawn, f'r th' Irish 'd 've skinned him alive if th' poor ol' gaby iv an English king hadn't ducked — What's that ? Don't I know it ? I have a book at home written be an impartial historyan, Pathrick Clancy Duffy, to prove it. What was I sayin' ? Whin' th' twelfth day iv July come around an' th' Orangeys got ready to cillybrate th' day King Willum, with all his Gatlin' guns an' cannon, just barely sthud off Sarsfield an' his men that had on'y pikes an' brickbats an' billyard cues, th' good people was infuryated. I dinnaw who was th' mayor in thim days. He was niver ilicted again. But, annyhow, he give it out that th' Orangeys' procission must not be hurted. An' all th' newspapers asked th' good people to be quite, an' it was announced at high mass an' low mass that annywan that sthruck a blow 'd be excommunicated.

" Well, ye know how it is whin modheration is counselled, Jawn. Modheration is another name f'r murdheration. So they put two platoons iv polismin in front iv th' Orangeys an' three behind, an' a double column alongside ; an' away they wint.

" No wan intherfered with thim ; an' that didn't plaze Morgan Dempsey, who'd served his time a calker in a ship-yard. Bein' iv a injaneyous disposition, he made up his mind f'r to do something to show that pathrietism wasn't dead in this counthry. So he got up in a hallway in Washington Sthreet, an' waited. Th' procission come with th' polismen in front an' behind an' along th' sides, an' th' German Band, thryin' to keep wan

eye on the house-tops on both sides iv th'
sthreet, an' to read th' music iv 'Lillibullero' an' 'Croppies lie down' an' 'Boyne
Wather' with th' other. Th' Orangeys
didn't look up. They kept their eyes
pointed sthraight ahead, I'll say that f'r
thim. They're murdherin' vilyans; but
they're Irish, iv a sort.

"Whin they come by Dempsey, he pokes
his head out iv th' dure; an' says he, 'Th'
'ell with all th' Prowtestant bishops.' Now
that same over in Derry'd have had all th'
tilin's in town flyin'; but th' Orangeys 'd
been warned not to fight, an' they wint
sthraight on, on'y they sung 'Lillibullero.'
Did ye niver hear it? It goes (*singing*)
'Ho! Brother Teigue, dost hear in th'
degree?'

"Th' Lord f'rgive me f'r singin' it, Jawn.
See if there's anny wan near th' dure.

"Well, whin they got through, Dempsey
puts his hands to his mouth, an' yells, 'Th'
'ell with King Willum.' That was more
thin th' Orangeys cud stand. They halted

as wan man, an' roared out, ' Th' 'ell with
th' pope.' ' What's that?' says th' captain
iv th' polis foorce. He was a man be th'
name of Murphy, an' he was blue with rage
f'r havin' to lead th' Orangeys. ' Ma-arch
on, Brass Money,' says th' Orange marshal.
Murphy pulled him fr'm his horse; an' they
wint at it, club an' club. Be that time th'
whole iv th' line was ingaged. Ivry copper
belted an Orangey; an' a sergeant named
Donahue wint through a whole lodge, armed
on'y, Jawn, with a clarinet an' wan cymbal.
He did so. An' Morgan Dempsey, th' cute
divvle, he sthood by, an' encouraged both
sides. F 'r, next to an Orangey, he likes to
see a polisman kilt. That ended wan Orangey parade.

"Not that I think it was right. I suppose they ought to be left walk about, an'
I'm a fair man. If th' blackest iv thim wint
by now, I'd not raise me hand " —

"Hello," says Mr. McKenna, " here goes
Killen, the Armagh man. They say he digs
with his left foot."

"Jawn," said Mr. Dooley, eagerly, "if ye run up on th' roof, ye'll find th' bricks loose in th' top row iv th' chimbley. Ye might hand him a few."

THE FREEDOM PICNIC.

"THERE'S wan thing about th' Irish iv this town," said Mr. Dooley.

"The police?" said Mr. McKenna.

"No," said the philosopher. "But they give picnics that does bate all. Be hivins, if Ireland cud be freed be a picnic, it 'd not on'y be free to-day, but an impire, begorra, with Tim Haley, th' Banthry man, evictin' Lord Salisb'ry fr'm his houldin'. 'Twud that.

"Jawn, th' la-ads have got th' thrick iv freein' Ireland down to a sinsible basis. In th' ol' days they wint over with dinnymite bumbs in their pockets, an' ayether got their rowlers on thim in Cork an' blew thimsilves up or was arristed in Queenstown f'r disordherly conduct. 'Twas a divvle iv a risky job to be a pathrite in thim days, an' none but those that had no wan dipindint on thim cud affoord it. But what was th' use? Ireland wint on bein' th' same opprissed green oil it had always been, an' th' on'y difference

th' rivolutions made was ye sa-aw new faces
on th' bridges an' th' Wolfe Tones passed
another set iv resolutions.

" 'Tis different now. Whin we wants
to smash th' Sassenach an' restore th' land
iv th' birth iv some iv us to her thrue place
among th' nations, we gives a picnic. 'Tis
a dam sight asier thin goin' over with a slug
iv joynt powder an' blowin' up a polis station with no wan in it. It costs less; an',
whin 'tis done, a man can lep aboord a sthreet
ca-ar, an' come to his family an' sleep it off.

" I wint out last Choosdah, an' I suppose
I must 've freed as much as eight counties in
Ireland. All th' la-ads was there. Th'
first ma-an I see was Dorgan, the sanyor
guarjeen in the Wolfe Tone Lithry Society.
He's th' la-ad that have made th' Prince iv
Wales thrimble in his moccasins. I heerd
him wanst makin' a speech that near injooced
me to take a bumb in me hand an' blow up
Westminsther Cathedral. 'A-re ye,' he
says, 'men, or a-re ye slaves?' he says.
'Will ye,' he says, 'set idly by,' he says,

'while th' Sassenach,' he says, 'has th'
counthry iv Immitt an' O'Connell,' he says,
'an' Jawn Im Smyth,' he says, 'undher his
heel?' he says. 'Arouse,' he says, 'slaves
an' despots!' he says. 'Clear th' way!' he
says. 'Cowards an' thraitors!' he says.
'Faugh-a-ballagh!' he says. He had th'
beer privilege at th' picnic, Jawn.

"Hinnissy, th' plumber, who blew wan iv
his fingers off with a bumb intinded f'r some
iv th' archytecture iv Liverpool, had th'
conthract f'r runnin' th' knock-th'-babby-
down-an'-get-a-nice-seegar jint. F'r th' good
iv th' cause I knocked th' babby down, Jawn,
an' I on'y wish th' Queen iv England 'r th'
Prince iv Wales cud be injooced to smoke
wan iv th' seegars. Ye might as well go
again a Roman candle. Th' wan I got was
made iv baled hay, an' 'twas rumored about
th' pa-ark that Hinnissy was wurrukin' off
his surplus stock iv bumbs on th' pathrites.
His cousin Darcey had th' shootin' gallery
privilege, an' he done a business th' like iv
which was niver knowed be puttin' up th'

figure iv an Irish polisman f'r th' la-ads to shoot at. 'Twas bad in th' end though, f'r a gang iv Tipp'rary lads come along behind th' tent an' begun thrown stones at th' copper. Wan stone hit a Limerick man, an' th' cry 'butthermilk' wint around; an' be hivins, if it hadn't been that th' chief iv polis, th' wise la-ad, sint none but German polismen to th' picnic, there'd not been a man left to tell th' tale."

"What's that all got to do with freeing Ireland?" asked Mr. McKenna.

"Well, 'tis no worse off thin it was befure, annyhow," said Mr. Dooley.

THE IDLE APPRENTICE.

"THEY hanged a man to-day," said Mr. Dooley.

"They did so," said Mr. McKenna.

"Did he die game?"

"They say he did."

"Well, he did," said Mr. Dooley. "I read it all in th' pa-apers. He died as game as if he was wan iv th' Christyan martyrs instead iv a thief that'd hit his man wan crack too much. Saint or murdherer, 'tis little difference whin death comes up face front.

"I read th' story iv this man through, Jawn; an', barrin' th' hangin', 'tis th' story iv tin thousan' like him. D'ye raymimber th' Carey kid? Ye do. Well, I knowed his grandfather; an' a dacinter ol' man niver wint to his jooty wanst a month. Whin he come over to live down be th' slip, 'twas as good a place as iver ye see. Th' honest men an' honest women wint as they pleased, an' laid hands on no wan. His boy Jim was as straight as th' r-roads in Kildare, but he took to dhrink; an', whin Jack Carey was born, he was a thramp on th' sthreets an' th' good woman was wurrukin' down-town, scrubbin' away at th' flures in th' city hall, where Dennehy got her.

" Be that time around th' slip was rough-an'-tumble. It was dhrink an' fight ivry night an' all day Sundah. Th' little la-ads come together under sidewalks, an' rushed th' can over to Burke's on th' corner an' listened to what th' big lads tol' thim. Th' first instruction that Jack Carey had was how to take a man's pocket handkerchief without his feelin' it, an' th' nex' he had was larnin' how to get over th' fence iv th' Reform School at Halsted Sthreet in his stockin' feet.

" He was a thief at tin year, an' th' polis 'd run f'r him if he'd showed his head. At twelve they sint him to th' bridewell f'r breakin' into a freight car. He come out, up to anny game. I see him whin he was a lad hardly to me waist stand on th' roof iv Finucane's Hall an' throw bricks at th' polisman.

"He hated th' polis, an' good reason he had f'r it. They pulled him out iv bed be night to search him. If he turned a corner, they ran him f'r blocks down th' sthreet. Whin he got older, they begun shootin' at him; an' it wasn't manny years befure he begun to shoot back. He was right enough whin he was in here. I cud conthrol him. But manny th' night whin he had his full iv liquor I've see him go out with his gun in his outside pocket; an' thin I'd hear shot after shot down th' sthreet, an' I'd know him an' his ol' inimy Clancy 'd met an' was exchangin' compliments. He put wan man on th' polis pension fund with a bullet through his thigh.

"They got him afther a while. He'd kept undher cover f'r months, livin' in freight cars an' hidin' undher viadocks with th' pistol in his hand. Wan night he come out, an' broke into Schwartzmeister's place. He sneaked through th' alley with th' German man's damper in his arms, an' Clancy leaped on him fr'm th' fence. Th' kid was tough,

but Clancy played fut-ball with th' Finerty's on Sundah, an' was tougher; an', whin
th' men on th' other beats come up, Carey
was hammered so they had to carry him to
th' station an' nurse him f'r trile.

"He wint over th' road, an come back
gray an' stooped. I was afraid iv th' boy
with his black eyes; an' wan night he see me
watchin' him, an' he says: 'Ye needn't be
afraid,' he says. 'I won't hurt ye. Ye're
not Clancy,' he says.

"I tol' Clancy about it, but he was a
brave man; an' says he: ''Tis wan an' wan,
an' a thief again an' honest man. If he gets
me, he must get me quick.' Th' nex' night
about dusk he come saunterin' up th' sthreet,
swingin' his club an' jokin with his frind,
whin some wan shouted, 'Look out, Clancy.'
He was not quick enough. He died face
forward, with his hands on his belt; an' befure all th' wurruld Jack Carey come across
th' sthreet, an' put another ball in his head.

"They got him within twinty yards iv me
store. He was down in th' shadow iv th'

house, an' they was shootin' at him fr'm roofs an' behind barns. Whin he see it was all up, he come out with his eyes closed, firin' straight ahead; an' they filled him so full iv lead he broke th' hub iv th' pathrol wagon takin' him to th' morgue."

"It served him right," said Mr. McKenna.

"Who?" said Mr. Dooley. "Carey or Clancy?"

THE O'BRIENS FOREVER.

"I THINK, by dad," said Mr. Dooley, "that Hinnissy's crazy."

"I always thought so," said Mr. McKenna, amiably. "But what's he been doin' of late?"

"Well, I took him down to see th' good la-ads havin' fun with th' opprissors iv th' people at th' Colliseem,' said Mr. Dooley. "I had no ticket, an' he had none. Th' frinds iv honest money had give thim all to Jawn P. Hopkins's la-ads. They're frinds iv honest money, whin they'se no other in sight. But I'd like to see anny goold-bug or opprissor iv th' people keep th' likes iv me an' Hinnissy out iv a convintion. We braced up to wan iv th' dures, an' a man stopped Hinnissy. 'Who ar-re ye?' he says. 'I am a Dimmycrat,' says Hinnissy. 'Is ye'er name Hill?' says th' la-ad. 'It is not,' says Hinnissy. 'I tol' ye I'm a Dimmycrat; an',' he says, 'I'll have no man call me out iv me name.' Hinnissy was f'r rollin' him on th' flure there an' thin f'r an insult, but I flagged a polisman. 'Is ye'er name Sullivan?' says I. 'It is,' says he. 'Roscommon?' says I, fr'm th' way he spoke. 'Sure ye're right,' he says. 'Me name's Dooley,' I says. 'Here,' say he to th' dure-keeper, 'don't stand in th' way iv th' sinitor iv th' State iv Mitchigan,' he says. 'Lave him an' his frind go in,' he says. I minded afther I was good to him whin Simon O'Donnell was chief iv polis, may he rest in peace!

"Hinnissy an' me got a seat be some dhroll ol' boys fr'm out in Iaway. Afther a man be th' name iv Martin, a sergeant-iv-arms, had addhressed th' meetin' twinty or thirty times,— I kep no count iv him,— th' chairman inthrojooced th' dillygates to nommynate th' big men. It wint all right with Hinnissy for a little while till a man got up an' shook his fist at th' chairman. 'What's that? what's that?' says Hinnissy. 'What's that?' he says. 'Hurroo, hurroo,' he says, lammin' th' man fr'm Iaway with his goold-headed cane. 'What ails ye, man alive?'

says I. 'Why,' he says, 'they've nommynated Billy,' he says. 'Billy who?' says I.
'Why, Willum J. O'Brien,' he says.

"'A sthrong man,' says he, addhressin'
th' man fr'm Iaway. 'I shud say he was,'
says th' man. 'Th' sthrongest man that
iver come down th' road,' says Hinnissy.
'Why,' he says, 'I see that man put up
an' eight iv beer with wan hand,' he says,
'holdin' it be th' rim,' he says. 'None
sthronger,' he says. 'But will he carry
Illinye?' says th' lad fr'm Iaway. 'Will
he carry Illinye?' says Hinnissy. 'Why,
man alive,' he says, 'I've see him carry
a prim'ry in th' sixth precint,' he says. 'Is
that enough f'r ye?' he says. 'He's a good
speaker,' says th' Iaway man. 'He is that,'
says Hinnissy; 'an' he was wan iv th' best
waltzers that flung a foot at th' County
Dimocracy picnic,' he says. 'But will he
make a good fight?' says th' man. 'Will
he?' says Hinnissy. 'Will he make a good
fight?' he says. 'Dooley,' he says, 'this
here Dimmycrat wants to know if Bill 'll

make a good fight. Why,' he says, 'if he
iver gets to Washington an' wan iv th'
opprissors iv th' people goes again him, give
him Jackson Park or a clothes closet, gun or
soord, ice-pick or billyard cue, chair or stove
leg, an' Bill 'll make him climb a tree,' he
says. 'I'd like to see wan iv thim supreme
justices again Bill O'Brien on an income tax
or anny other ord-nance,' he says. 'He'd
go in an' lame thim with th' Revised Statutes.'
'I presume,' says th' lad, 'that ye'er fr'm
Omaha.' 'I'll tear ye'er hair out,' says
Hinnissy.'

"'Ye idjit,' says I, whin I had him in th'
sthreet, 'it wasn't Bill O'Brien was nommynated,' says I. 'What ar-re ye talkin'
about?' says he. 'I seen him on th' flure,'
he says. 'He had th' sinitor iv Missoury
be th' throat whin ye took me away,' he
says.

"I left him there; but he come into th'
place at six o'clock, an' borrid a paper an'
pencil. Thin he wint back, an' sat down an'
wrote. 'What ar-re ye doin' there?' says

I. 'I've wrote a sketch iv th' nominee f'r th' Stock-yards Sun,' he says. 'Listen to it. Willum J. O'Brien,' he says, 'was born in th' County iv Mayo forty years ago,' he says. 'He received a limited education, his parents even thin designin' him f'r th' Prisidency. Bein' unable to complete a coorse at th' rayform school, he wint to wurruk; but soon, tired iv this, he started a saloon. Fr'm thince he dhrifted into politics, an' become noted as th' boy welter-weight iv th' South Branch. He was ilicted aldherman at a time whin comparatively nawthin' was doin' in th' council. Subse-quent he become a sinitor, an' later enthered into partnership with th' Hon. Jawn Powers in th' retail liquor traffic. Mr. O'Brien is a fine built man, an' can lick anny wan iv his age west iv th' river, give 'r take tin pounds, color no bar. His heart bets up close to th' ribs iv th' common people, an' he would make opprissors iv th' poor wish they'd died early if ye give him a chance with a beer bottle. How's that?' says Hinnissy.

"'Worse,' says I. 'Foolish man,' says I. 'Don't ye know that it ain't our Bill that's been nommynated?' I says. 'This is a Nebraska man,' I says. 'Well,' he says, 'if 'tis Bill O'Brien, he'd win easy. But,' he says, 'if 'tis not,' he says, ''tis wan iv th' fam'ly,' he says. 'I'll change this here novel an' make it a sketch iv th' cousin iv th' candydate,' he says. An' he wint on with his wurruk."

A CANDIDATE'S PILLORY.

"What's this counthry comin' to, anny-how, that a man that's out f'r to be President has to set up on a high chair an' be questioned on his record be a lot iv la-ads that hasn't had annything to do since th' carpet-beatin' season's ended?" said Mr. Dooley. "Ye'd think Big Bill was r-runnin' f'r chief ex-icutive iv th' Clan-na-Gael. First along comes a comity iv th' Sons iv Rest. 'Major,' says they, 'we're insthructed be th' organiza-tion to ascertain ye'er views on th' important, we may say all-important, question iv havin' wire matthresses put on th' benches in th' parks. Are we,' they says, 'goin' f'r to have to wear lumps on our backs into all eternity,' they says, 'an' have our slumbers broke be th' hot fut iv th' polisman?' they says. 'We demand an answer,' they says, 'or, be this an' be that, we won't do a thing to ye.' Well, maybe Bill has been down to th' corner playin' a game iv spoil-five with his old frind Coalsack, an' has paid no attintion to th' Sons iv Rest. 'Well,' he says, 'gintlemen, I'm in favor iv doin' ivrything in reason f'r th' hoboes,' he says. 'Th' protection iv th' home hobo again th' pauper can trade iv Europe,' he says, 'has been wan iv th' principal wurruks iv me life,' he says; an' he gives thim each a hand out, an' bows thim to th' dure.

"In comes a dillygation fr'm th' Union iv Amalgamated Pantsmakers; an' says th' chairman, 'Major,' he says, 'we have a complaint to make again thim pants iv ye'ers,' he says. 'What's th' matter with th' pants?' says th' future Prisident. 'I thought they looked all right,' he says. 'I paid four dollars f'r thim in Bucyrus las' year,' he says. 'They have no union label on thim,' says th' chairman. 'Do you know, sir,' he says, 'that thim pants riprisints th' oppression iv women an' childher?' he says. 'D'ye know that ivry thread in thim seams means a tear an' sigh?' says he. 'D'ye know that ivry time ye put on thim pants ye take a pair off some down-throdden

workman?' he says. 'Glory be!' says Big
Bill: 'is that thrue? Thin what am I to
do?' he says in alarm. 'Do?' says th'
chairman. 'Wear pants that riprisints honest toil fairly compinsated,' he says. 'Wear
pants that'll say to th' wurruld that Bill
McKinley's legs are fair legs;' he says, 'that
they may bow at th' knees, but they niver
bow to th' opprissor,' he says; 'that niver
did they wrap thimsilves in bags that bore
th' curse iv monno-poly an' greed,' he says.
'An' where can I get thim?' says th' major.
'Fr'm me,' says th' frind iv labor, pullin'
out a tape. 'Will ye have wan or two hip
pockets?' he says.

"An' so it goes. Ivry day a rayporther
comes to th' house with a list iv questions.
'What are ye'er views on th' issue iv eatin'
custard pie with a sponge? Do ye believe in
side-combs? If called upon to veto a bill
f'r all mimbers iv th' Supreme Coort to wear
hoop-skirts, wud ye veto it or wudden't ye?
If so, why? If not, why not? If a batted
ball goes out iv th' line afther strikin' th'

player's hands, is it fair or who? Have ye that tired feelin'? What is your opinion iv a hereafter? Where did you get that hat? If a man has eight dollars an' spends twelve iv it, what will th' poor man do? An' why an' where an' how much?'

"Thin, if he don't answer, ivry wan says he's a thrimmer, an' ought to be runnin' a sthreet-car an' not thryin' to poke his onde-cided face into th' White House. I mind wanst, whin me frind O'Brien was a candy-date f'r aldherman, a comity iv tax-payers waited on him f'r to get his views on th' issues iv th' day. Big Casey, th' house-mover, was th' chairman; an' he says, says he, 'Misther O'Brien,' he says, 'we are desirous,' he says, 'iv larnin' where ye stand on th' tariff, th' currency question, pensions, an' th' intherstate commerce act,' he says, with a wave iv his hand. 'Well,' says O'Brien, he says, 'th' issue on which I'm appealin' to th' free an' intilligent suffrages of Ar-rchey Road an' th' assistance iv Deerin' Sthreet Station,' he says, 'is whether little

Mike Kelly will have th' bridge or not,' he
says. 'On that I stand,' he says. 'As f'r
th' minor issues,' he says, 'I may have me
opinions on thim an' I may not. Anny information I possess I'll keep tucked away in
this large an commodjous mind cage, an' not
be dealin' it out to th' likes iv ye, as though
I was a comity iv th' Civic Featheration,' he
says. 'Moreover,' he says, 'I'd like to
know, you, Casey, what business have you
got comin' roun' to my house and pryin' into
my domestic affairs,' he says. ''Tis th'
intherstate commerce act now, but th' nex'
thing'll be where I got th' pianny,' he says;
'an', f'r fear ye may not stop where ye are,
here goes to mount ye.' An' he climbed th'
big man, an' rolled him. Well, sir will ye
believe me, ivry man on th' comity but wan
voted f'r him. Casey was still in bed iliction day.

"I met Tom Dorsey afther th' comity
called. 'Well,' says I, 'I heerd ye was up
to O'Brien's questionin' him on th' issues iv
th' day,' I says. 'We was,' says he. 'Was

his answers satisfacthry?' says I. 'Perfectly so,' he says. 'Whin th' comity left, we were all convinced that he was th' strongest man that cud be nommynated,' he says."

THE DAY AFTER THE VICTORY.

"JAWN," said Mr. Dooley, "didn't we give it to thim?"

"Give it to who?" asked Mr. McKenna.

"To th' Dimmycrats," said Mr. Dooley.

"Go on," said Mr. McKenna. "You're a Democrat yourself."

"Me?" said Mr. Dooley, "not on your life. Not in wan hundherd thousand years. Me a Dimmycrat? I shud say not, Jawn, me buck. I'm the hottest kind iv a Raypublican, me an' Maloney. I suppose they ain't two such Raypublicans annywhere. How can anny wan be annything else? Who was it that saved the Union, Jawn? Who was it? Who are th' frinds iv th' Irish? Who protecks th' poor wurrukin'man so that he'll have to go on wurrukin'? We do, Jawn. We Raypublicans, by dad.

"They ain't a Dimmycrat fr'm wan end iv th' road to th' other. I just was over makin' a visit on Docherty, an' he'd took down th' picture iv Jackson an' Cleveland

an' put up wan iv Grant an' Lincoln.
Willum Joyce have come out f'r McKinley
f'r Prisident, an' th' polisman on th' beat
told me las' night that th' left'nant told
him that 'twas time f'r a change. Th' Dimm-
mycrats had rooned th' counthry with their
free trade an' their foreign policy an' their I
dinnaw what, an' 'twas high time an honest
man got a crack at a down-town precinct with
a faro bank or two in it. Th' polisman
agreed with him that Cleveland have raised
th' divvle with th' Constitootion ; an', by
gar, he's right, too. He's right, Jawn. He
have a boy in th' wather office.

"Ye mind Maloney, th la-ad with th'
game eye? He tends a bridge over be
Goose Island way, but he was down here
iliction day. Two weeks befure iliction day
he was again Winter. 'He's no good,' he
says. 'He's a Boohemian,' he says. 'An'
whin they come to ilictin' Boohemians f'r
mayor,' he says, 'I'll go back to me ol'
thrade iv shovelin' mud,' he says. 'Besides,' says he, 'if this here Winter wint in,'

he says, 'ye cudden't stand acrost La Salle
Street an' hand him a peach on a window
pole, he'd be that stuck up,' he says.

"Some wan must 've spoke to him; f'r,
whin he come in th' next time, he says,
'They'se no use talkin',' he says, 'that there
Dutchman is sthrong,' he says. 'I thought
he was a Boolgahrian,' says I. 'No,' says
he, 'he's a German man,' says he. 'An' th'
Germans is with him to th' bitther end,' he
says. 'D'ye know,' he says, 'I believe he'll
give th' little bald-headed duck a run f'r his
money,' he says. 'Thim Germans stand
together,' he says. 'They're th' most clan-
nish people on earth,' he says. 'I'm goin'
over to th' Wolfe Tones to see what th'
la-ads think about it.' Sundah night he
come an' give a ca-ard f'r Winter to ivry
man in th' place. 'He'll sweep th' town
like a whirlwind,' he says. 'They can't
beat him.' 'Who?' says I. 'Winter, iv
coorse.' 'Is he a nice man?' says I. 'Wan
iv th' finest men on earth,' he says. 'A
spoort, too,' he says. 'An' liberal.'

' He was in here iliction day, an' I had
Hinnissy's kid runnin' fr'm th' station with
rayturns.   Maloney was talkin' to th' crowd
an' buyin' dhrinks. ' Ye'd be surprised,'
says he, ' to know what a nice fellow this here
Winter is,' he says. ' Ye'd niver take him
f'r a German,' he says. ' He have no more
accint thin mesilf.'   The kid come in, an'
says he, ' Th' loot says tin precincts show
Swift have a majority as big as what th'
Raypublicans got las' fall.' ' That's bad,'
says I. ' Not at all,' says Maloney.
' Thim's th' down-town wa-ards,' he says.
' Wait till ye hear fr'm th' Germans,' he
says.   Th' nex' booletin said Swift was
gainin', an' had tin thousand majority.
' Niver mind,' says Maloney. ' Th' Germans 'll wipe that out,' he says.   Thin we
heerd it was twinty thousand f'r Swift.
' Glory be,' says Maloney, ' th' Germans is
slow comin' in,' he says. ' Maybe,' says I,
' they forgot to vote,' says I. ' Maybe
they're havin' a schootzenfist,' I says, ' an'
are out killin' clay pigeons instid iv attendin''

to business,' I says. Just thin th' loot
come in. 'Well,' says he, ''tis quite a
Waterloo,' says he. 'F'r who?' says I.
'Oh,' he says, 'Swift got it be forty thousand.'

"Maloney wiped his face, and took off
his hat an' swabbed it inside. Thin says
he: 'D'ye raymimber me meetin' ye down-
town a week ago on Dorney's place, loot?'
he says. 'Yes,' says th' loot. 'D'ye mind
what I said thin?' he says. 'I don't call it
just now,' says the loot. 'Well, I just come
fr'm a meetin' iv th' Swift Marchin' Club, an'
I niver seen so much enthusyasm; an' I says
to ye, I says: 'Loot,' I says, 'Swift 'll bate
him aisy,' I says. 'I knew he would fr'm th'
beginnin'. Ye take an' put up a good broad
liberal man like George B., a man that has
frinds an' knows how to be a good fellow,
an' run him again a Boohemian gazabo
who gives ivry man th' marble heart an' 'd
turn down his own brother, an' anny fool
cud tell who'd win. They'll be some chance
f'r a man with Swift over there; but, if this

here Winter wint in, ye cudden't stand acrost
La Salle Sthreet an' hand him a peach on th'
end iv a window pole,' he says.

"Will he lose his job? Not much, Jawn.
That la-ad 'll be swingin' bridges an' throwin' away th' crust iv his pie whin you an' me
are atin' ha-ard coal. He will that. But
what do I care? Machs nix aus, Jawn; an'
that being translated manes, ' What th'
'ell.' "

A VISIT TO JEKYL ISLAND.

"I'd like to been there," said Mr. Dooley.

"Where's that?" Mr. Hennessy asked.

"At Shekel Island," said Mr. Dooley, "seein' me frind Mack an' me frind Tom Reed meetin' be th' sad sea waves.

"Ye see, Mack was down there with Mark Hanna. He was tired out with expandin', an' anxiety f'r fear me frind Alger 'd ray-sign; an' says Hanna, he says, 'Come down,' he says, 'with me,' he says, 'to Shekel Island,' he says. ''Tis th' home iv rayfine-mint an' riches,' he says, 'where us mill-yionaires rest fr'm takin' care iv th' coun-thry,' he says. 'There in th' shade iv th' coupon threes,' he says, 'we watch th' sea waves, an' wondher,' he says, 'whin th' goold that's in thim can be exthracted,' he says. 'They'se nawthin' to break th' silence,' he says, 'but th' roarin' iv th ocean,' he says; 'an' that sounds nat'ral,' he says, 'because 'tis almost like th' sound iv th' stock ex-change,' he says. 'A man,' he says, 'that has th' ticker eye,' he says, 'or th' coupon thumb,' he says, 'is cured in no time,' he says. 'Come,' he says, 'fly with me,' he says. 'They'se nawthin' to keep ye here,' he says. 'Ivry wan iv th' cab'net, includin' th' Sicrety iv War, 'll stick to his place,' he says, 'like a man,' he says.

"An' Mack wint with him. He was set-tin' on th' beach in a goold chair, surrounded be millyionaires, with th' prisident iv a bank fannin' him an' th' threeasurer iv a dimon' mine poorin' his dhrink; an', though he was feelin' well, they was something on his mind. 'What ails ye?' ast Hanna. 'I was thinkin',' says Mack, 'how pleasant 'twud be if me ol' frind Tom Reed was here,' he says. ''Twud be Paradise if he was here,' he says, whin, lo an' behold, who shud come acrost th' dimon'-studded beach, wadin' through th' bank-notes that'd been dropped be th' good farmers iv Shekel Island, but Tom Reed.

"Well, sir, to see th' affection that those two great men showed at th' encounther 'd dhraw tears fr'm th' eyes iv a hear-rt iv sthone. 'Tom,' says Mack, in fal.herin' accints, 'where have ye been? F'r days an' days I've skinned yon blue horizon f'r anny sign iv ye,' he says. 'An' ye come not,' he says. 'I didn't think I cud miss ye so,' he says. 'Embrace me,' he says, 'if ye ar-re not ar-rmed,' he says. 'Mack,' says me frind Tom Reed, with tears in his eyes, 'this,' he says, 'is th' happiest moment iv me life,' he says. 'I cudden't,' he says, 'I cudden't stay in Wash'nton,' he says, 'with you so far away,' he says, 'where I cudden't watch ye,' he says. 'Ye're th' on'y man in th' wurruld I care f'r,' he says, 'but mesilf.' he says. 'An',' he says, 'I'd fall weepin' on ye'er shoulder this minyit,' he says; 'but I don't want to be disrayspectful be turnin' me back on Misther Hanna,' he says.

"'Well,' says Mack, 'sit down,' he says. 'Rockyfeller,' he says, 'tell Morgan f'r to fetch up a kag iv sherry wine,' he says. 'Tom,' he says, 'we've been frinds f'r years,' he says. 'We have,' says Tom. 'We've

concealed it fr'm th' vulgar an' pryin' public,' he says ; 'but in our hear-rts we've been
frinds, barrin' th' naygur dillygates at th'
convintion,' he says. ''Twas a mere inci-
dent,' says Mack. 'We've been frinds,' he
says ; 'an' I've always wanted,' he says, 'to
do something f'r ye,' he says. 'Th' time
has come,' he says, 'whin I can realize me
wish,' he says. 'I offer ye,' he says, 'th'
Prisidincy, to succeed me,' he says. 'No,
no,' he says, 'I'll not be rayfused,' he says.
'I'm tired iv it,' he says. ''Twas foorced
on me be foolish frinds,' he says ; 'but I'm
not th' man f'r th' place,' he says. 'I
haven't dhrawn a comfortable breath, not to
speak iv salary, since I wint in,' he says.

"Th' speaker iv th' house burrid his face
in his hands, an' sobs shook him partly f'r
manny minyits. Thin he raised his head, an'
says he, 'Mack,' he says, 'I can't take it,'
he says. ''Tis most gin'rous iv ye,' he says,
'but me hear-rt fails me,' he says. 'What
is it to be Prisident?' says he. 'Th' White
House,' he says, 'is a prison,' he says, 'to

which a man is condimned,' he says, ' f'r
fine wurruk at th' polls,' he says. 'Th' life
iv a Prisident is slavery,' he says. ' If I was
to take th' job,' he says, 'I'd be tortured
day an' night,' he says, ' be th' fear iv assas-
sination,' he says. 'Think,' he says, 'iv
some arnychist shootin' thirteen-inch shells
at me,' he says, 'an' maybe,' he says, 'dent-
in' me,' he says. ' No,' he says, ' I have a
good job where I am,' he says. ' All I've
got to do,' he says, 'is to set up at th' desk,'
he says, 'an' not recall th' names iv th' gin-
tlemin on th' flure, an' me jooty's done,' he
says. ' I thank ye kindly, Willum; but
I cannot accept ye'er gin'rous offer,' he
says. ' Go back to th' cell,' he says, 'an'
slave like a convict,' he says. ' I will not
rob me frind,' he says, ' iv such an honor.
But,' he says, 'tell me whin ye thought iv
throwin' up th' job, an' lavin' me br-reak
into this hateful prison,' he says. 'About
th' year two thousan' an' eight, dear frind,'
says Mack. ' No, no,' says Tom Reed.
' I cannot accept it,' he says, pressin'

Mack's hand. ''Tis too much,' he says, 'an' too long,' he says.

"'I lave ye,' he says, 'but I'll call on ye,' he says. 'Take,' he says, 'this little silver-mounted bottle iv broomo-caffeen,' he says, 'an' think iv me,' he says. 'I will,' says Mack. 'Ar-ren't ye tired iv ye'er long journey?' he says. 'Wudden't ye like to take a bath in th' shark pond befure ye go?' he says. An' so they backed away fr'm each other, th' tears rollin' down their cheeks. Frindship, Hinnissy, is a sacred thing."

"It is," said Mr. Hennessy, "if they are; but I don't b'lieve wan wurrud ye tol' me."

"Well," said Mr. Dooley, "if they ain't both frinds, wan iv thim is. An', annyhow, I'm glad to know Tom Reed ain't thryin' to break into jail."

SLAVIN CONTRA WAGNER.

"Ol' man Donahue bought Molly a pianny las' week," Mr. Dooley said in the course of his conversation with Mr. McKenna. "She'd been takin' lessons fr'm a Dutchman down th' sthreet, an' they say she can play as aisy with her hands crossed as she can with wan finger. She's been whalin' away iver since, an' Donahue is dhrinkin' again.

"Ye see th' other night some iv th' la-ads wint over f'r to see whether they cud smash his table in a frindly game iv forty-fives. I don't know what possessed Donahue. He niver asked his frinds into the parlor befure. They used to set in th' dining-room ; an', whin Mrs. Donahue coughed at iliven o'clock, they'd toddle out th' side dure with their hats in their hands. But this here night, whether 'twas that Donahue had taken on a dhrink or two too much or not, he asked thim all in th' front room, where Mrs. Donahue was settin' with Molly.

'I've brought me frinds,' he says, 'f'r to hear Molly take a fall out iv th' music-box,' he says. 'Let me have ye'er hat, Mike,' he says. 'Ye'll not feel it whin ye get out,' he says.

"At anny other time Mrs. Donahue'd give him th' marble heart. But they wasn't a man in th' party that had a pianny to his name, an' she knew they'd be throuble whin they wint home an' tould about it. ''Tis a mel-odjious insthrument,' says she. 'I cud sit here be the hour an' listen to Bootoven and Choochooski,' she says.

"'What did thim write?' says Cassidy. 'Chunes,' says Donahue, 'chunes. Molly,' he says, 'fetch 'er th' wallop to make th' gintlemen feel good,' he says. 'What'll it be, la-ads?' 'D'ye know "Down be th' Tan-yard Side"?' says Slavin. 'No,' says Molly. 'It goes like this,' says Slavin. 'A-ah, din yadden, yooden a-yadden, arrah yadden ay-a.' 'I dinnaw it,' says th' girl. ''Tis a low chune, annyhow,' says Mrs. Donahue. 'Misther Slavin ividintly thinks

he's at a polis picnic,' she says. 'I'll have
no come-all-ye's in this house,' she says.
'Molly, give us a few ba-ars fr'm Wagner.'
'What Wagner's that?' says Flanagan.
'No wan ye know,' says Donahue; 'he's
a German musician.' 'Thim Germans is
hot people f'r music,' says Cassidy. 'I
knowed wan that cud play th' "Wacht am
Rhine" on a pair iv cymbals,' he says.
'Whisht!' says Donahue. 'Give th' girl a
chanst.'

"Slavin tol' me about it. He says he
niver heerd th' like in his born days. He
says she fetched th' pianny two or three
wallops that made Cassidy jump out iv his
chair, an' Cassidy has charge iv th' steam
whistle at th' quarry at that. She wint at it
as though she had a gredge at it. First
'twas wan hand an' thin th' other, thin both
hands, knuckles down; an' it looked, says
Slavin, as if she was goin' to leap into th'
middle iv it with both feet, whin Donahue jumps up. 'Hol' on!' he says.
'That's not a rented pianny, ye daft girl,' he

says. 'Why, pap-pah,' says Molly, 'what d'ye mean?' she says. 'That's Wagner,' she says. ''Tis th' music iv th' future,' she says. 'Yes,' says Donahue, 'but I don't want me hell on earth. I can wait f'r it,' he says, 'with th' kind permission iv Mrs. Donahue,' he says. 'Play us th' " Wicklow Mountaineer,"' he says, 'an' threat th' masheen kindly,' he says. 'She'll play no " Wicklow Mountaineer,"' says Mrs. Donahue. 'If ye want to hear that kind iv chune, ye can go down to Finucane's Hall,' she says, 'an' call in Crowley, th' blind piper,' she says. 'Molly,' she says, 'give us wan iv thim Choochooski things,' she said. 'They're so ginteel.'

"With that Donahue rose up. 'Come on,' says he. 'This is no place f'r us,' he says. Slavin, with th' politeness iv a man who's gettin' even, turns at th' dure. 'I'm sorry I can't remain,' he says. 'I think th' wurruld an' all iv Choochooski,' he says. 'Me brother used to play his chunes,' he says,—'me brother Mike, that run th' grip ca-ar,' he says. 'But there's wan thing missin' fr'm Molly's playin', he says. 'And what may that be?' says Mrs. Donahue. 'An ax,' says Slavin, backin' out.

"So Donahue has took to dhrink."

GRAND OPERA.

"Jawn," said Mr. Dooley, "'tis a gr-reat thing to be a polisman. Me frind Doheny, what used to be at Deerin' Sthreet, have got on th' crossin', an' they've planted him down be th' Audjitooroom. He was up here las' week, an' says he, 'Run in, an' look at th' op'ra,' says he. 'Run in, an' take a flash iv it,' he says. ''Tis gr-reat,' he says. So I takes Duggan, an' we goes down together.

"Well, Doheny does be gr-reat paper with thim. He was standin' be th' dure, with white gloves over his hands; an', whin we come, he give th' office to th' la-ad on th' gate, an' says th' la-ad, 'Sure thing,' he says. 'Sure thing,' an' in we goes. They was a lot iv Gazoorios there, some iv thim settin' in seats an' some iv thim in bur-rd cages up above, an' more standin'. Thim standin' was th' la-ads that Doheny rushed in. Ye niver see such a lot iv thim, — Cassidy, O'Regan, Hogan, Mulcahey, Shay, Mullaney, Mullvihill, an' th' eight

O'Neills,— all sint through be Doheny
without cridintials. Sure, it looked like a
meetin' iv th' Wolf Tones. It did that.

"Th' op'ra was on whin we wint in, an'
they was whalin' away in Eyetallian. Duggan listened; an' says he, 'What's the man
sayin'?' he says. 'I dinnaw,' I says. 'He's
talkin' Chinese, an',' says I, 'they're goin' to
sind him to th' laundhry,' says I. 'Look,'
I says. 'They're puttin' him in th' clothes-
basket,' I says. 'If they do,' says he,
'he'll niver come back,' he says, 'or else
he'll have another name,' he says. 'Let's
buy a scoor ca-ard,' says he. So he bought
wan, an' was r-readin' it an' lookin' over th'
top iv it at th' women in th' boxes, an' wondhrin' why some wan didn't tell thim their
dhresses was slippin' down, whin over comes
Cassidy, and says he, 'What's th' news in
th' Sixth?' 'Nawthin,' says Duggan.
'Will O'Brien win?' says Cassidy. 'They
can't beat him,' says Duggan. 'I dinnaw,'
says Cassidy. 'Come over here, an' I'll tell
ye,' says Duggan. Dinny Shay an' Hogan

an' Mullaney jined us, an' we wint an' set on
the steps.

"'Can Winter beat Swift?' says Shay.
'I'd like to know,' says Hogan. 'I don't
know who to vote f'r,' he says; 'an' Mike
is in th' wather office,' he says. ''Tis a
cinch Hinky'll win out in th' First,' says
Mullaney. 'He have a sthrong man again
him,' says Hogan. 'Gleason have wan or
two lodgin'-houses.' 'Three,' says Shay;
'but Hinkey knows all th' lodgers,' he says.
''Twas a mane thing th' main guy done with
Callaghan,' says Hogan. 'What's that?'
says Shay. 'Thrun him off th' bridge,'
says Hogan, 'because he come fr'm Kerry,'
he says. 'I don't believe wan wurrud iv it,'
says Mullaney. 'They're more Kerry men
on bridges thin anny other counties,' he
says. 'What has bet Hopkins,' he says, 'is
his frindship fr'm th' Mayo men,' he says.
'Th' Mayo men is great f'r carryin' prim'-
ries, afther they're over,' he says. 'But
did anny wan iver hear iv thim doin' anny
good whin th' votes was bein' cast?' 'I

knowed wan that did,' says Cassidy, as black as ye'er boot. 'His name was Cassidy,' he says; 'an' he done some good,' he says, 'be privintin' a man be th' name iv Mullaney,' he says, 'fr'm bein' a dilligate.' 'Ye had th' polis with ye,' says Mullaney. 'Ye was supported be th' fire departmint,' says Cassidy.

"'Let's change th' subject,' says Duggan. 'What show has Dorsey got in th' Twinty-ninth? 'None at all,' says wan iv th' O'Neills who'd come over. 'He have th' Civic Featheration again him.' 'Who cares f'r th' Civic Featheration?' says Mulcahey. 'They don't vote,' he says. 'What'll kill Dorsey,' he says, 'is his bein' an Apee-a.' 'He's no Apee-a,' says Mike O'Neill. 'I wint to th' Brothers' school with him,' he says. 'Whiniver a man comes up that can't be downed anny way, he's called an Apee-a,' he says. 'He's no more an Apee-a thin ye are,' he says. 'D'ye mean to call me that?' says Mulcahey. 'Come out, an' have a dhrink,' I says; an' we wint down.

"Well, Jawn, we had wan iv th' liveliest political argumints ye iver see without so much as a blow bein' sthruck. Evenly matched, d'ye mind, with a chair f'r ivry man. An' th' bar-tinder was a frind iv mine. I knowed him whin he was with Schwartz-meister. A good la-ad,— a good lad."

"But what about th' opera?" asked Mr. McKenna.

"Th op'ra wus gr-reat," said Mr. Dooley; "but I think Mulcahey was right. Dorsey can't win."

THE CHURCH FAIR.

"Wanst I knew a man," said Mr. Dooley, laying down his newspaper, "be th' name iv Burke, that come fr'm somewhere around Derry, though he was no Presbyteryan. He was iv th' right sort. Well, he was feelin' how-come-ye-so, an' he dhrifted over to where we was holdin' a fair. They was a band outside, an' he thought it was a grand openin'. So he come in with a cigar in th' side iv his mouth an' his hat hangin' onto his ear. It was th' last night iv th' fair, an' ivrything was wide open; f'r th' priest had gone home, an' we wanted f'r to break th' record. This Burke was f'r lavin' whin he see where he was; but we run him again th' shootin' gallery, where ye got twinty-five cints, a quarther iv a dollar, f'r ivry time ye rang th' bell. Th' ol' gun we had was crooked as a ram's horn, but it must 've fitted into Burke's squint; f'r he made that there bell ring as if he was a conducthor iv a grip-car roundin' a curve. He

had th' shootin' gallery on its last legs whin
we run him again th' wheel iv fortune.   He
broke it.   Thin we thried him on th' grab-
bag.   They was four goold watches an' anny
quantity iv brickbats an' chunks iv coal in
th' bag.   He had four dives, an' got a watch
each time.   He took a chanst on ivrything;
an' he won a foldin'-bed, a doll that cud talk
like an old gate, a pianny, a lamp-shade, a
Life iv St. Aloysius, a pair iv shoes, a base-
ball bat, an ice-cream freezer, an' th' pomes
iv Mike Scanlan.

  " Th' comity was disthracted.   Here was
a man that 'd break th' fair, an' do it with th'
best iv humor; f'r he come fr'm another
parish.   So we held a private session.
' What 'll we do? ' says Dorgan, th' chairman.   They was a man be th' name iv
Flaherty, a good man thin an' a betther now;
f'r he's dead, may he rest in peace!   An'
Flaherty says : ' We've got to take th' bull
be th' horns,' he says.   ' If ye lave him to
me,' he says, ' I'll fix him,' he says.

  So he injooced this man Burke to come

down back iv th' shootin' gallery, an' says he
to Burke, 'Ye're lucky to-night.' 'Not so
very,' says Burke. ''Twud be a shame to
lave ye get away with all ye won,' says
Flaherty. ''Twill be a great inconvanience,'
says Burke. 'I'll have to hire two or three
dhrays,' he says; 'an' 'tis late.' 'Well,' says
Flaherty, 'I'm appinted be th' parish to
cut th' ca-ards with ye,' he says, 'whether
ye're to give back what ye won or take
what's left.' ''Tis fair,' says Burke; 'an',
whoiver wins, 'tis f'r a good cause.' An' he
puts th' watches an' th' money on th' table.

"'High man,' says Flaherty. 'High
man,' says Burke. Flaherty cut th' king iv
spades. Burke, th' robber, cut th' ace iv
hearts. He was reachin' out f'r th' money,
whin Flaherty put his hands over it. 'Wud
ye take it?' says he. 'I wud,' says Burke.
'Wud ye rob th' church?' says Flaherty.
'I wud,' says Burke. 'Thin,' says Flaherty,
scoopin' it in, 'ye're a heretic; an' they'se
nawthin' comin' to ye.'

"Burke looked at him, an' he looked at

th' comity; an' he says, 'Gintlemen, if iver ye come over in th' Sixth Ward, dhrop in an' see me,' he says. 'I'll thry an' make it plisint f'r ye,' he says. An' he wint away.

"Th' story got out, an' th' good man heerd iv it. He was mighty mad about it; an' th' nex' sermon he preached was on th' evils iv gamblin', but he asked Flaherty f'r to take up th' colliction."

THE WANDERERS.

"Poor la-ads, poor la-ads," said Mr. Dooley, putting aside his newspaper and rubbing his glasses. "'Tis a hard lot theirs, thim that go down into th' sea in ships, as Shakespeare says. Ye niver see a storm on th' ocean? Iv coorse ye didn't. How cud ye, ye that was born away fr'm home? But I have, Jawn. May th' saints save me fr'm another! I come over in th' bowels iv a big crazy balloon iv a propeller, like wan iv thim ye see hooked up to Dempsey's dock, loaded with lumber an' slabs an' Swedes. We watched th' little ol' island fadin' away behind us, with th' sun sthrikin' th' white house-tops iv Queenstown an' lightin' up th' chimbleys iv Martin Hogan's liquor store. Not wan iv us but had left near all we loved behind, an' sare a chance that we'd iver spoon th' stirabout out iv th' pot above th' ol' peat fire again. Yes, by dad, there was wan,—a lad fr'm th' County Roscommon. Divvle th' tear he shed. But, whin we had

parted fr'm land, he turns to me, an' says,
' Well, we're on our way,' he says. ' We
are that,' says I. ' No chanst f'r thim to
turn around an' go back,' he says. ' Divvle
th' fut,' says I. ' Thin,' he says, raisin' his
voice, ' to 'ell with th' Prince iv Wales,' he
says. ' To 'ell with him,' he says.

"An' that was th' last we see of sky or
sun f'r six days. That night come up th'
divvle's own storm. Th' waves tore an'
walloped th' ol' boat, an' th' wind howled,
an' ye cud hear th' machinery snortin' beyant. Murther, but I was sick. Wan time
th' ship 'd be settin' on its tail, another it 'd
be standin' on its head, thin rollin' over
cow-like on th' side ; an' ivry time it lurched
me stummick lurched with it, an' I was tore
an' rint an' racked till, if death come, it 'd
found me willin'. An' th' Roscommon man,
— glory be, but he was disthressed. He set
on th' flure, with his hands on his belt an'
his face as white as stone, an' rocked to an'
fro. ' Ahoo,' he says, ' ahoo, but me insides
has torn loose,' he says, ' an' are tumblin'
around,' he says. ' Say a pather an' avy,'

says I, I was that mad f'r th' big bosthoon f'r his blatherin'. 'Say a pather an'
avy,' I says; f'r ye're near to death's dure,
avick.' 'Am I?' says he, raising up.
'Thin,' he says, 'to 'ell with the whole rile
fam'ly,' he says. Oh, he was a rebel!

"Through th' storm there was a babby
cryin'. 'Twas a little wan, no more thin a
year ol'; an' 'twas owned be a Tipp'rary
man who come fr'm near Clonmel, a poor,
weak, scarey-lookin' little divvle that lost
his wife, an' see th' bailiff walk off with th'
cow, an' thin see him come back again with
th' process servers. An' so he was comin'
over with th' babby, an' bein' mother an'
father to it. He'd rock it be th' hour on
his knees, an' talk nonsense to it, an'
sing it songs, 'Aha, 'twas there I met a
maiden,' an' 'Th' Wicklow Mountaineer,'
an' 'Th' Rambler fr'm Clare,' an' 'O'Donnel
Aboo,' croonin' thim in th' little babby's
ears, an' payin' no attintion to th' poorin'
thunder above his head, day an' night, day
an' night, poor soul. An' th' babby cryin'
out his heart, an' him settin' there with his

eyes as red as his hair, an' makin' no kick, poor soul.

"But wan day th' ship settled down steady, an' ragin' stummicks with it; an' th' Roscommon man shakes himself, an' says, 'To 'ell with th' Prince iv Wales an' th' Dook iv Edinboroo,' an' goes out. An' near all th' steerage followed; f'r th' storm had done its worst, an' gone on to throuble those that come afther, an' may th' divvle go with it. 'Twill be rest f'r that little Tipp'rary man; f'r th' waves was r-runnin' low an' peaceful, an' th' babby have sthopped cryin'.

"He had been settin' on a stool, but he come over to me. 'Th' storm,' says I, 'is over. 'Twas wild while it lasted,' says I. 'Ye may say so,' says he. 'Well, please Gawd,' says I, 'that it left none worse off thin us.' 'It blew ill f'r some an' aise f'r others,' says he. 'Th' babby is gone.'

"An' so it was, Jawn, f'r all his rockin' an' singin'. An' in th' avnin' they burried it over th' side into th' sea. An' th' little man see thim do it."

MAKING A CABINET.

"I SUPPOSE, Jawn," said Mr. Dooley, "ye do be afther a governmint job. Is it council to Athlone or what, I dinnaw?"

"I haven't picked out the place yet," said Mr. McKenna. "Bill wrote me the day after election about it. He says: 'John,' he says, 'take anything you want that's not nailed to the wall,' he says. He heard of my good work in the Twenty-ninth. We rolled up eight votes in Carey's precinct, and had five of them counted; and that's more of a miracle than carrying New York by three hundred thousand."

"It is so," said Mr. Dooley. "It is f'r a fact. Ye must 've give the clerks an' judges morphine, an' ye desarve great credit. Ye ought to have a place; an' I think ye'll get wan, if there's enough to go round among th' Irish Raypublicans. 'Tis curious what an effect an iliction has on th' Irish Raypublican vote. In October an Irish Raypublican's so rare people point him out

on th' sthreet, an' women carry their babies
to see him.   But th' day afther iliction, glory
be, ye run into thim ivrywhere,— on th'
sthreet-car, in the sthreet, in saloons princi-
pally, an' at th' meetin's iv th' Raypublican
Comity.   I've seen as manny iv them as
twinty in here to-day, an' ivry wan iv thim
fit to run anny job in th' governmint, fr'm
directin' th' Departmint iv State to carryin'
ashes out an' dumpin thim in th' white lot.

  " They can't all have jobs, but they've
got to be attinded to first; an', whin Mack's
got through with thim, he can turn in an'
make up that cabinet iv his.   Thin he'll
have throuble iv his own, th' poor man, on'y
comin' into fifty thousand a year and rint free.
If 'twas wan iv th' customs iv th' great raypublic iv ours, Jawn, f'r to appoint th' most
competent men f'r th' places, he'd have a
mighty small lot f'r to pick fr'm.   But, seein'
that on'y thim is iligible that are unfit, he has
th' divvle's own time selectin'.   F'r Sicrety
iv State, if he follows all iv what Casey calls
recent precidints, he's limited to ayether a

jack-leg counthry lawyer, that has set around
Washington f'r twinty years, pickin' up a
dollar or two be runnin' errands f'r a foreign
imbassy, or a judge that dóesn't know
whether th' city of Booloogne-sure-Mere,
where Tynan was pinched, is in Boolgahria
or th' County Cavan. F'r Sicrety iv th'
Threasury he has a choice iv three kinds iv
proud and incompetent fi-nanceers. He can
ayether take a bank prisident, that 'll see
that his little bank an' its frinds doesn't get
th' worst iv it, or a man that cudden't main-
tain th' par'ty iv a counthry dhry-good store
long enough to stand off th' sheriff, or a
broken-down Congressman, that is full iv red
liquor half the year, an' has remorse settin'
on his chest th' other half.

"On'y wan class is iligible f'r Attorney-
gin'ral. To fill that job, a man's got to be
a first-class thrust lawyer. If he ain't, th'
Lord knows what 'll happen. Be mistake he
might prosecute a thrust some day, an' th'
whole counthry'll be rooned. He must be
a man competint f'r to avoid such pitfalls

an' snares, so 'tis th' rule f'r to have him
hang on to his job with th' thrust afther he
gets to Washington. This keeps him in
touch with th' business intherests.

"F'r Sicrety iv War, th' most like wan is
some good prisident iv a sthreet-car company. 'Tis exthraordinney how a man learns
to manage military affairs be auditin' thrip
sheets an' rentin' signs in a sthreet-car to
chewin' gum imporyums. If Gin'ral Washington iv sacred mimory 'd been under a
good sthreet-car Sicrety iv War, he'd 've wore
a bell punch to ring up ivry time he killed
a Hessian. He wud so, an' they'd 've kep'
tab on him, an', if he thried to wurruk a
brother-in-law on thim, they'd give him his
time.

"F'r th' Navy Departmint ye want a
Southern Congressman fr'm th' cotton belt.
A man that iver see salt wather outside iv
a pork bar'l 'd be disqualified f'r th' place.
He must live so far fr'm th' sea that he
don't know a capstan bar fr'm a sheet
anchor. That puts him in th' proper

position to inspect armor plate f'r th' immi-
nent Carnegie, an' insthruct admirals that's
been cruisin' an' fightin' an' dhrinkin' mint
juleps f'r thirty years. He must know th'
difference bechune silo an' insilage, how to
wean a bull calf, an' th' best way to cure
a spavin. If he has that information, he is
fixed f'r th' job.

"Whin he wants a good Postmaster-gin-
'ral, take ye'er ol' law partner f'r awhile,
an', be th' time he's larned to stick stamps,
hist him out, an' put in a school-teacher fr'm
a part iv th counthry where people commu-
nicate with each other through a conch.
Th' Sicrety iv th' Interior is an important
man. If possible, he ought to come fr'm
Maine or Florida. At anny rate, he must
be a resident iv an Atlantic seacoast town,
an' niver been west iv Cohoes. If he gets
th' idee there are anny white people in Ann
Arbor or Columbus, he loses his job.

"Th' last place on th' list is Sicrety iv
Agriculture. A good, lively business man
that was born in th' First Ward an' moved to

th' Twinty-foorth after th' fire is best suited
to this office.   Thin he'll have no preju-
dices against sindin' a farmer cactus seeds
whin he's on'y lookin' f'r wheat, an' he will
have a proper understandin' iv th' importance iv an' early Agricultural Bureau rayport to th' bucket-shops.

" No Prisident can go far away that follows Cleveland's cabinet appintmints, al-
though it may be hard f'r Mack, bein' new
at th' business, to select th' right man f'r th'
wrong place.   But I'm sure he'll be advised
be his frinds, an' fr'm th' lists iv candydates
I've seen he'll have no throuble in findin'
timber."

OLD AGE.

"Skatin'," said Mr. Dooley, "was in- tinded f'r th' young an' gay. 'Tis not f'r th' likes iv me, now that age has crept into me bones an' whitened th' head iv me. Divvle take th' rheumatics! An' to think iv me twenty years ago cuttin' capers like a bally dancer, whin th' Desplaines backed up an' th' pee-raires was covered with ice fr'm th' mills to Riverside. Manny's th' time I done th' thrick, Jawn, me an' th' others; but now I break me back broachin' a kag iv beer, an' th' height iv me daily exercise is to wind th' clock befure turnin' in, an' count up th' cash."

"You haven't been trying to skate?" Mr. McKenna asked in tones of alarm.

"Not me," said Mr. Dooley. "Not me, but Hinnissy have. Hinnissy, th' gay young man; Hinnissy, th' high-hearted, divvle-may-care sphread-th'-light,— Hin- nissy's been skatin' again. May th' Lord give that man sinse befure he dies! An' he needs it right away. He ain't got long to live, if me cousin, Misther Justice Dooley, don't appoint a garjeen f'r him.

"I had no more thought whin I wint over with him that th' silly goat 'd thry his pranks thin I have iv flyin' over this here bar mesilf. Hinnissy is — let me see how ol' Hinnissy is. He was a good foot taller thin me th' St. John's night whin th' comet was in th' sky. Let me see, let me see! Jawn Dorgan was marrid to th' widdy Casey (her that was Dora O'Brien) in th' spring iv fifty-two, an' Mike Callahan wint to Austhreelia in th' winter iv sixty. Hinnissy's oldest brother was too old to inlist in th' army. Six an' thirty is thirty-six. Twict thirty-six is sivinty-two, less eight is sixty-four, an' nine, carry wan,— let me see. Well, Hinnissy is ol' enough to know betther.

"We wint to th' pond together, an' passed th' time iv day with our frinds an' watched th' boys an' girls playin' shinny an' sky-larkin' hand in hand. They come separate,

Jawn; but they go home together, thim
young wans. I see be his face Spoort Hinnissy was growin' excited. 'Sure,' says he,
'there's nawthin' like it,' he says. 'Martin,'
he says, 'I'll challenge ye to race,' he says.
'So ye will,' says I. 'So ye will,' I says.
'Will ye do it?' says he. 'Hinnissy,' says
I, 'come home,' I says, 'an' don't disgrace
ye'er gray hairs befure th' whole parish,'
says I. 'I'll have ye to know,' says he,
'that 'tis not long since I cud cut a double
eight with anny wan in Bridgeport,' he says.

"At that Tom Gallagher's young fly-be-
night joined in; an' says he, 'Misther Hinnissy,' he says, 'if ye'll go on,' he says, 'I'll
fetch ye a pair iv skates.' 'Bring thim
along,' says Hinnissy. An' he put thim on.
Well, Jawn, he sthud up an' made wan step,
an' wan iv his feet wint that way an' wan
this; an' he thrun his hands in th' air, an'
come down on his back. I give him th'
merry laugh. He wint clear daft, an' thried
to sthruggle to his feet; an', th' more he
thried, th' more th' skates wint fr'm undher

him, till he looked f'r all th' wurruld like wan iv thim little squirrels that goes roun' on th' wheel in Schneider's burrud store.

"Gallagher's lad picked him up an' sthud him on his feet; an' says he, politely, 'Come on,' he says, 'go roun' with me.' Mind ye, he took him out to th' middle iv th' pond, Hinnissy movin' like a bridge horse on a slippery thrack; an' th' lad shook him off, an' skated away. 'Come back!' says Hinnissy. 'Come back!' he says. 'Tom, I'll flay ye alive whin I catch ye on th' sthreet! Come here, like a good boy, an' help me off. Dooley,' he roars to me, 'ain't ye goin' to do annything?' he says. 'Ne'er a thing,' says I, 'but go home.' 'But how'm I goin' to cross?' he says. 'Go down on ye'er knees an' crawl,' says I. 'Foolish man!' I says. An' he done it, Jawn. It took him tin minyits to get down in sections, but he done it. An' I sthud there, an' waited f'r him while he crawled wan block over th' ice, mutterin' prayers at ivry fut.

"I wint home with him afterwards; an'

what d'ye think he said? 'Martin,' says he,
'I've been a sinful man in me time; but I
niver had th' like iv that f'r a pinance,' he
says. 'Think iv doin' th' stations iv th'
cross on th' ice,' he says. 'Hinnissy,' I
says, 'they'se no crime in th' catalogue akel
to bein' old,' I says. 'Th' nearest thing to
it,' I says, 'is bein' a fool,' I says; 'an' ye're
both,' I says."

THE DIVIDED SKIRT.

"Jawn," said Mr. Dooley, "did ye iver hear th' puzzle whin a woman's not a woman?"

"Faith, I have," said Mr. McKenna. "When I was a kid, I knew the answer."

"Ye didn't know this answer," said Mr. Dooley. "Whin is a woman not a woman? 'Twas give to me las' Satthurdah night be young Callaghan, th' sthreet-car man that have all th' latest jokes that does be out. Whin is a woman not a woman? mind ye. Whin's she's on a bicycle, by dad. Yes, yes. Whin she's on a bicycle, Jawn. D'ye know Molly Donahue?"

"I know her father," said Mr. McKenna.

"Well, well, the dacint man sint his daughter Molly to have a convint schoolin'; an' she larned to pass th' butther in Frinch an' to paint all th' chiny dishes in th' cubb'rd, so that, whin Donahue come home wan night an' et his supper, he ate a green paint ha-arp along with his cabbage, an' they had to sind

f'r Docthor Hinnissy f'r to pump th' a-art
work out iv him. So they did. But Donahue, bein' a quite man, niver minded that,
but let her go on with her do-se-does an'
bought her a bicycle. All th' bicycles th'
poor man had himsilf whin he was her age
was th' dhray he used to dhrive f'r Comis-
key; but he says, ' 'Tis all th' thing,' he says.
' Let th' poor child go her way,' he says to
his wife, he says. ' Honoria,' he says, ' she'll
get over it.'

" No wan knowed she had th' bicycle, because she wint out afther dark an' practised
on it down be th' dump. But las' Friday
evnin', lo an' behold, whin th' r-road was
crowded with people fr'm th' brick-yards an'
th' gas-house an' th' mills, who shud come
ridin' along be th' thracks, bumpin' an'
holdin' on, but Molly Donahue? An'
dhressed! How d'ye suppose she was
dhressed? In pa-ants, Jawn avick. In
pa-ants. Oh, th' shame iv it! Ivry wan on
th' sthreet stopped f'r to yell. Little Julia
Dorgan called out, ' Who stole Molly's

dhress?' Ol' man Murphy was settin'
asleep on his stoop. He heerd th' noise, an'
woke up an' set his bull tarrier Lydia Pink-
ham on her. Malachi Dorsey, vice-prisi-
dent iv th' St. Aloysius Society, was comin'
out iv th' German's, an' see her. He put
his hands to his face, an' wint back to th'
house.

"But she wint bumpin' on, Jawn, till she
come up be th' house. Father Kelly was
standin' out in front, an' ol' man Donahue
was layin' down th' law to him about th'
tariff, whin along come th' poor foolish girl
with all th' kids in Bridgeport afther her.
Donahue turned white. 'Say a pather an'
avy quick,' he says to the priest. Thin he
called out to his wife. 'Honoria,' he says,
'bring a bar'l,' he says. 'Molly has come
away without annything on,' he says, 'but
Sarsfield's pa-ants.' Thin he turned on his
daughter. 'May th' Lord forgive ye,
Molly Donahue,' he says, 'this night!' he
says. 'Child, where is ye'er dhress?'
'Tut, tut!' says th' good man. 'Molly,' he

says, 'ye look well on that there bicycle,' he
says. 'But 'tis th' first time I ever knowed
ye was bow-legged,' he says, says th' soggarth aroon.

"Well, sir, she wint into th' house as if
she'd been shot fr'm a gun, an' th' nex'
mornin' I see Doheny's express wagon
haulin' th' bicycle away."

"Didn't Father Kelly do anything about
it?" asked Mr. McKenna.

"No," replied Mr. Dooley. "There was
some expicted she'd be read fr'm th' altar at
high mass, but she wasn't."

A BIT OF HISTORY.

MR. McKENNA found Mr. Dooley standing at the end of his bargain counter with the glasses on the tip of his nose. He was in deep contemplation of a pile of green paper which he was thumbing over.

"Jawn," said he, as Mr. McKenna walked over and looked on curiously, "d'ye know a good man that I cud thrust to remodel th' shop?"

"And what's got into you?" asked Mr. McKenna.

"I'm goin' to have two large mirrors put on th' side an' wan below. Thin I'm goin' to have th' ceilin' painted green, an' a bull-yard table put in th' back room. 'Twill be a place to par'lyze ye whin it is through with."

"And what 'll pay for it?" asked Mr. McKenna, in blank amazement.

"This," said Mr. Dooley, whacking the pile before him. "Here's twinty thousand dollars iv th' bonds iv th' raypublic. They

bear inthrest at twinty-five per cint.; an'
they're signed be Xavier O'Malley, Pagan
O'Leary (th' wicked man), an' O'Brien, th'
threeasurer. Me cousin Mike put thim up
with me f'r a loan iv five. He wurruked in
th' threeasurer's office; an', whin th' polis
broke up th' Irish rivolution, he put on his
coat an' stuck a month's bond issue in his
pocket. 'They'll come in handy wan day,'
he says; for he was a philosopher, if he did
take a dhrop too much. Whin he give me
th' bonds, he says, says he, 'Hol' to thim,'
he says, 'an' some time or other they'll
make a rich man iv ye.' Jawn, I feel th'
time has come. Cleveland's on th' rampage;
an', if Ireland ain't a raypublic befure a
month, I'll give ye these here documents f'r
what I paid on thim. I have me information fr'm Hinnissy, an' Hinnissy have it
fr'm Willum Joyce, an' ye know how close
Joyce is to Finerty. Hinnissy was in last
night. 'Well,' says I, 'what's th' news?' I
says. 'News?' says he. 'They'se on'y
wan thing talked about,' he says. 'We're

goin' to have a war with England,' he says. 'An' th' whole Irish army has inlisted,' he says. 'Has Finerty gone in?' says I. 'He has,' he says. 'Thin,' says I, ''tis all off with th' Sassenach. We'll run thim fr'm th' face iv th' earth,' I says. ''Tis th' prisint intintion iv mesilf to hire a good big tug an' put a hook into Ireland, an' tow it over th' big dhrink, an' anchor it ayether in th' harbor iv New York or in th' lake.

"D'ye know, Jawn, 'twas Cleveland that definded th' Fenians whin they was took up f'r invadin' Canada. 'Twas so. He was not much in thim days,— a kid iv a lawyer, like Doheny's youngest, with a lot iv hair an' a long coat an' a hungry look. Whin th' Fenians come back fr'm Canada in a boat an' landed in th' city iv Buf-falo, New York, they was all run in; an' sare a lawyer cud they get to defind thim till this here Cleveland come up, an' says he: 'I'll take th' job,' he says. 'I'll go in an' do th' best I can f'r ye.' Me uncle Mike was along with thim, an' he looked Cleveland

over; an' says he: 'Ye'll do th' best ye can
f'r us,' he says, 'will ye?' he says. 'Well,'
he says, 'I'll take no chances,' he says.
'Sind f'r th' desk sergeant,' he says. 'I'm
goin' to plead guilty an' turn informer,' he
says. 'Tis lucky f'r Cleveland me uncle
died befure he r-run f'r President. He'd 've
had wan vote less.

"I'll niver forget th' night me uncle
Mike come back fr'm Canada. Ye know
he was wan iv th' most des'prit Fenians that
iver lived; an', whin th' movement begun,
he had to thread on no wan's shadow befure
he was off f'r th' battle. Ivry wan in town
knew he was goin'; an' he wint away with a
thrunk full iv bottles an' all th' good wishes
iv th' neighborhood, more be reason iv th'
fact that he was a boistherous man whin he
was th' worse f'r wear, with a bad habit iv
throwin' bricks through his neighbors'
windys. We cud see him as th' thrain
moved out, walkin' up an' down th' aisle,
askin' iv there was anny Englishman in th'
car that 'd like to go out on th' platform an'
rowl off with him.

" Well, he got up in New York an' met a lot iv other des'prite men like himsilf, an' they wint across th' bordher singin' songs an' carryin' on, an' all th' militia iv New York was undher ar-rms; f'r it 'd been just like thim to turn round an' do their fightin' in New York. 'Twas little me uncle Mike cared where he fought.

" But, be hook or crook, they got to where th' other Fenians was, an' jined th' army. They come fr'm far an' near; an' they were young an' old, poor lads, some iv thim bent on sthrikin' th' blow that 'd break th' back iv British tyranny an' some jus' crazed f'r fightin'. They had big guns an' little guns an' soord canes an' pitchforks an' scythes, an' wan or two men had come over armed with baseball bats. They had more gin'rals thin ye cud find in a Raypublican West Town convintion, an' ivry private was at laste a colonel. They made me uncle Mike a brigadier gin'ral. ' That'll do f'r a time,' says he; ' but, whin th' fun begins, I'll pull Dorney off his horse, an' be

a major gin'ral,' he says.   An' he'd 've done
it, too, on'y they was no fightin'.

"They marched on, an' th' British run
away fr'm thim; an', be hivins, me uncle Mike
cud niver get a shot at a redcoat, though he
searched high an' low f'r wan.   Thin a big
rain-storm come, an' they was no tents to
protect thim; an' they set aroun', shiverin'
an' swearin'.   Me uncle Mike was a bit iv
a politician; an' he organized a meetin' iv th'
lads that had come over with him, an' sint
a comity to wai on th' major gin'ral.
'Dorney,' says me uncle Mike, f'r he was
chairman iv th' comity, 'Dorney,' he says,
'me an' me associated warriors wants to
know,' he says.   'What d'ye mane?' says
Dorney.   'Ye brought us up here,' says
me uncle Mike, 'to fight the British,' he
says.   'If ye think,' he says, 'that we
come over,' he says, 'to engage in a six
days' go-as-you-please walkin' match,' he
says, 'ye'd betther go an' have ye'er head
looked into,' he says.   'Have ye anny British around here?   Have ye e'er a Sassenach

concealed about ye'er clothes?' he says. 'We can't do annything if they won't stand f'r us,' says Dorney. 'Thin,' says me uncle Mike, 'I wash me hands iv th' whole invasion,' he says. 'I'll throuble ye f'r me voucher,' he says. 'I'm goin back to a counthry where they grow men that 'll stand up an' fight back,' he says; an' he an' his la-ads wint over to Buf-falo, an' was locked up f'r rivolution.

"Me uncle Mike come home on th' bumpers iv a freight car, which is th' way most rivolutioners come home, excipt thim that comes home in th' baggage car in crates. 'Uncle Mike,' says I to him, 'what's war like, annyhow?' 'Well,' says he, 'in some rayspicts it is like missin' th' last car,' he says; 'an' in other rayspicts 'tis like gettin' gay in front iv a polis station,' he says. An', by dad, whin I come to think what they call wars nowadays, I believe me uncle Mike was right. 'Twas diff'rent whin I was a lad. They had wars in thim days that was wars."

THE RULING CLASS.

" I SEE be th' pa-apers," said Mr. Dooley,
"that arnychy's torch do be lifted, an' what
it means I dinnaw; but this here I know,
Jawn, that all arnychists is inimies iv governmint, an' all iv thim ought to be hung f'r
th' first offence an' bathed f'r th' second.
Who are they, annyhow, but foreigners, an'
what right have they to be holdin' torchlight
procissions in this land iv th' free an' home
iv th' brave? Did ye iver see an American
or an Irishman an arnychist? No, an' ye
niver will. Whin an Irishman thinks th'
way iv thim la-ads, he goes on th' polis force
an' dhraws his eighty-three-thirty-three f'r
throwin' lodgin'-house bums into th' pathrol
wagon. An' there ye a-are.

"'I niver knowed but th' wan arnychist,
an' he was th' divvle an' all f'r slaughtherin'
th' rich. He was a Boolgahrian man that
lived down be Cologne Sthreet, acrost th'
river; but he come over to Bridgeport whin
he did have his skates on him, f'r th' liftenant

over there was again arnychists, an' 'twas little our own Jawnny Shea cared f'r thim so long as they didn't bother him. Well, sir, this here man's name was Owsky or something iv that sort, but I always called him Casey be way iv a joke. He had whiskers on him like thim on a cokynut, an' I heerd he swore an oath niver to get shaved till he killed a man that wore a stove-pipe hat.

"Be that as it may, Jawn, he was a most ferocious man. Manny's th' time I've heerd him lecture to little Matt Doolan asleep like a log behind th' stove. 'What a-are we comin' to?' he'd say. 'What a-are we comin' to?' D'ye mind, Jawn, that's th' way he always began. 'Th' poor do be gettin' richer,' says he, 'an' th' rich poorer,' says he. 'Th' governmint,' says he, 'is in th' hands iv th' monno-polists,' he says, 'an' they're crushin' th' life out iv th' prolo-toorios.' A prolotoorio, Jawn, is th' same thing as a hobo. 'Look at th' Willum Haitch Vanderbilts,' says he, 'an' th' Gools an' th' Astors,' says he, 'an' thin look at us,' he says, 'groun' down,' he says, 'till we cries f'r bread on th' sthreet,' he says; 'an' they give us a stone,' he says. 'Dooley,' he says, 'fetch in a tub iv beer, an' lave th' collar off,' he says.

"Doolan 'd wake up with a start, an' applaud at that. He was a little tailor-man that wurruked in a panthry down town, an' I seen him weep whin a dog was r-run over be a dhray. Thin Casey 'd call on Doolan f'r to stand his ground an' desthroy th' polis,— 'th' onions iv th' monno-polists,' he called thim,— an' Doolan 'd say, 'Hear, hear,' till I thrun thim both out.

"I thought me frind Casey 'd be taken up f'r histin' a polisman f'r sure, though, to be fair with him, I niver knowed him to do but wan arnychist thing, and that was to make faces at Willum Joyce because he lived in a two-story an' bay-window brick house. Doolan said that was goin' too far, because Willum Joyce usually had th' price. Wan day Casey disappeared, an' I heerd he was married. He niver showed up f'r a year; an', whin he come in, I hardly knowed him. His whiskers had been filed an' his hair cut, an' he was dhressed up to kill. He wint into th' back room, an' Doolan was asleep there. He woke him, an' made a speech to him that was full iv slaughther and blood-shed. Pretty soon in come a little woman, with a shawl over her head,—a little German lady. Says she, 'Where's me hoos-band?' in a German brogue ye cud cut with an ax. 'I don't know ye'er husband, ma'am,' says I. 'What's his name?' She told me, an' I seen she was Casey's wife. 'He's in there,' I says. 'In back,' I says, 'talking to Doolan, th' prolotoorio.' I wint back with her, an' there was Casey whalin' away. 'Ar-re ye men or ar-re ye slaves?' he says to Doolan. 'Julius,' says his wife, 'vat ye doin' there, ye blackgaard,' she says. 'Comin' ze, or be hivens I'll break ye'er jaw,' she says. Well, sir, he turned white, an' come over as meek as a lamb. She grabbed him be th' arm an' led him off, an' 'twas th' last I seen iv him.

"Afther a while Doolan woke up, an' says he, 'Where's me frind?' 'Gone,' says I. 'His wife came in, an' hooked him off.' 'Well,' says Doolan, ''tis on'y another victhry iv the rulin' classes,' he says."

THE OPTIMIST.

"Aho," said Mr. Dooley, drawing a long, deep breath. "Ah-ho, glory be to th' saints!"

He was sitting out in front of his liquor shop with Mr. McKenna, their chairs tilted against the door-posts. If it had been hot elsewhere, what had it been in Archey Road? The street-car horses reeled in the dust from the tracks. The drivers, leaning over the dash-boards, flogged the brutes with the viciousness of weakness. The piles of coke in the gas-house yards sent up waves of heat like smoke. Even the little girls playing on the sidewalks were flaming pink in color. But the night saw Archey Road out in all gayety, its flannel shirt open at the breast to the cooling blast and the cries of its children filling the air. It also saw Mr. Dooley luxuriating like a polar bear, and bowing cordially to all who passed.

"Glory be to th' saints," he said, "but it's been a thryin' five days. I've been mean enough to commit murdher without th' strength even to kill a fly. I expect to have a fight on me hands; f'r I've insulted half th' road, an' th' on'y thing that saved me was that no wan was sthrong enough to come over th' bar. 'I cud lick ye f'r that, if it was not so hot,' said Dorsey, whin I told him I'd change no bill f'r him. 'Ye cud not,' says I, 'if 'twas cooler,' I says. It's cool enough f'r him now. Look, Jawn dear, an' see if there's an ice-pick undher me chair.

"It 'd be more thin th' patience iv Job 'd stand to go through such weather, an' be fit f'r society. They's on'y wan man in all th' wurruld cud do it, an' that man's little Tim Clancy. He wurruks out in th' mills, tin hours a day, runnin' a wheelbarrow loaded with cindhers. He lives down be-yant. Wan side iv his house is up again a brewery, an' th' other touches elbows with Twinty-Percint Murphy's flats. A few years back they found out that he didn't own on'y th' front half iv th' lot, an' he can set on his

back stoop an' put his feet over th' fince
now. He can, faith. Whin he's indures,
he breathes up th' chimbley; an' he has a
wife an' eight kids. He dhraws wan twenty-
five a day — whin he wurruks.

"He come in here th' other night to talk
over matthers; an' I was stewin' in me shirt,
an' sayin' cross things to all th' wurruld fr'm
th' tail iv me eye. ''Tis hot,' says I. ''Tis
war-rum,' he says. ''Tis dam hot,' says I.
'Well,' he says, ''tis good weather f'r th'
crops,' he says. 'Things grows in this
weather. I mind wanst,' he says, 'we had
days just like these, an' we raised forty
bushels iv oats to an acre,' he says. 'Whin
Neville, th' landlord, come with wagons to
take it off, he was that surprised ye cud iv
knocked him down with a sthraw. 'Tis
great growin' weather,' he says. An', Jawn,
by dad, barrin' where th' brewery horse spilt
oats on th' durestep an' th' patches iv grass
on th' dump, sare a growin' thing but childher has that little man seen in twinty years.

"'Twas hotter whin I seen him nex', an'
I said so. ''Tis war-rum,' he says, laughin'.

'By dad, I think th' ice 'll break up in th' river befure mornin',' he says. 'But look how cold it was last winter,' he says. 'Th' crops need weather like this,' he says. I'd like to have hit him with a chair. Sundah night I wint over to see him. He was sittin' out in front, with a babby on each knee. 'Good avnin',' says I. 'Good avnin',' he says. 'This is th' divvle's own weather,' I says. 'I'm suffocatin'.' ''Tis quite a thaw,' he says. 'How's all th' folks?' says I. 'All well, thank ye kindly,' he says, 'save an' except th' wife an' little Eleen,' he says. 'They're not so well,' he says. 'But what can ye expect? They've had th' best iv health all th' year.' 'It must be har-rd wurrukin' at th' mills this weather,' I says. ''Tis war-rum,' he says; 'but ye can't look f'r snow-storms this time iv th' year,' he says. 'Thin,' says he, 'me mind's taken aff th' heat be me wurruk,' he says. 'Dorsey that had th' big cinder-pile — the wan near th' fence — was sun-struck Fridah, an' I've been promoted to his job. 'Tis a most re-sponsible place,' he says; 'an' a man, to fill it rightly an' properly, has no time to think f'r th' crops,' he says.   An' I wint away, lavin' him singin' 'On th' Three-tops' to th' kids on his knees.

"Well, he comes down th' road tonight afther th' wind had turned, with his old hat on th' back iv his head, whistlin' 'Th' Rambler fr'm Clare' and I stopped to talk with him. 'Glory be,' says I, ''tis pleasant to breathe th' cool air,' says I. 'Ah,' he says, ''tis a rale good avnin',' he says. 'D'ye know,' he says, 'I haven't slept much these nights, f'r wan reason 'r another.   But,' he says, 'I'm afraid this here change won't be good f'r th' crops,' he says. 'If we'd had wan or two more war-rum days an' thin a sprinkle iv rain,' he says, 'how they would grow, how they would grow!'"

Mr. Dooley sat up in his chair, and looked over at Mr. McKenna.

"Jawn," he said, "d'ye know that, whin I think iv th' thoughts that's been in my head f'r a week, I don't dare to look Tim Clancy in th' face."

PROSPERITY.

"Th' defeat iv Humanity be Prosperity was wan iv th' raysults iv th' iliction," said Mr. Dooley.

"What are you talking about?" asked Mr. McKenna, gruffly.

"Well," said Mr. Dooley, "I thought it was McKinley an' Hobart that won out, but I see now that it's McKinley an' Prosperity. If Bryan had been elected, Humanity would have had a front seat an' a tab. Th' sufferin's iv all th' wurruld would have ended; an' Jawn H. Humanity would be in th' White House, throwin' his feet over th' furniture an' receivin' th' attintions iv diplomats an' pleeniapotentiaries. It was decided otherwise be th' fates, as th' Good Book says. Prosperity is th' bucko now. Barrin' a sthrike at th' stock-yards an' a hold-up here an' there, Prosperity has come leapin' in as if it had jumped fr'm a springboard. Th' mills are opened, th' factories are goin' to go, th' railroads are watherin' stocks, long

processions iv workin'men are marchin'
fr'm th' pay-car to their peaceful saloons,
their wives are takin' in washin' again, th'
price iv wheat is goin' up an' down, creditors
are beginnin' to sue debtors; an' thus all th'
wurruld is merry with th' on'y rational
enjoyments iv life.

"An' th' stock exchange has opened.
That's wan iv th' strongest signs iv prosperity. I min' wanst whin me frind Mike
McDonald was controllin' th' city, an' con-
ductin' an exchange down be Clark Sthreet.
Th' game had been goin' hard again th'
house. They hadn't been a split f'r five
deals. Whin ivrybody was on th' queen to
win, with th' sivin spot coppered, th' queen
won, th' sivin spot lost. Wan lad amused
himsilf be callin' th' turn twinty-wan times
in succession, an' th' check rack was down
to a margin iv eleven whites an' fifty-three
cints in change. Mike looked around th'
crowd, an' turned down th' box. 'Gintlemen,' says he, 'th' game is closed. Business conditions are such,' he says, 'that I

will not be able to cash in ye'er checks,' he
says. ' Please go out softly, so 's not to dis-
turb th' gintlemen at th' roulette wheel,' he
says, ' an' come back afther th' iliction, whin
confidence is restored an' prosperity returns
to th' channels iv thrade an' industhry,' he
says. ' Th' exchange 'll be opened promptly ;
an' th' usual rule iv chips f'r money an'
money f'r chips, fifty on cases an' sivinty-
five f'r doubles, a hard-boiled egg an' a
dhrink f'r losers, will prevail,' he says.
' Return with th' glad tidings iv renewed
commerce, an' thank th' Lord I haven't took
ye'er clothes.' His was th' first stock exchange we had.

"Yes, Prosperity has come hollerin' an
screamin'. To read th' papers, it seems to
be a kind iv a vagrancy law. No wan can
loaf anny more. Th' end iv vacation has
gone f'r manny a happy lad that has spint
six months ridin' through th' counthry,
dodgin' wurruk, or loafin' under his own vine
or hat-three. Prosperity grabs ivry man
be th' neck, an' sets him shovellin' slag or

coke or runnin' up an' down a ladder with
a hod iv mortar. It won't let th' wurruld
rest. If Humanity 'd been victoryous, no
wan 'd iver have to do a lick again to th' end
iv his days. But Prosperity's a horse iv
another color. It goes round like a polisman givin' th' hot fut to happy people that
are snoozin' in th' sun. 'Get up,' says
Prosperity. 'Get up, an' hustle over to th'
rollin' mills : there's a man over there wants
ye to carry a ton iv coal on ye'er back.' 'But
I don't want to wurruk,' says th' lad. 'I'm
very comfortable th' way I am.' 'It makes
no difference,' says Prosperity. 'Ye've got
to do ye'er lick. Wurruk, f'r th' night is
comin'. Get out, an' hustle. Wurruk, or
ye can't be unhappy; an', if th' wurruld isn't
unhappy, they'se no such a thing as Prosperity.'

"That's wan thing I can't understand,"
Mr. Dooley went on. "Th' newspapers is
run be a lot iv gazabos that thinks wurruk
is th' ambition iv mankind. Most iv th'
people I know 'd be happiest layin' on a

lounge with a can near by, or stretchin'
thimsilves f'r another nap at eight in th'
mornin'. But th' papers make it out that
there'd be no sunshine in th' land without
you an' me, Hinnissy, was up befure daybreak
pullin' a sthreet-car or poundin' sand with a
shovel. I seen a line, ' Prosperity effects on
th' Pinnsylvania Railroad'; an' I read on to
find that th' road intinded to make th' men
in their shops wurruk tin hours instead iv
eight, an' it says 'there's no reasons why
they should not wurruk Sundahs iv they
choose.' If they choose! An' what chance
has a man got that wants to make th' wurruld
brighter an' happier be rollin' car-wheels but
to miss mass an' be at th' shops?"

"We must all work," said Mr. McKenna,
sententiously.

"Yes," said Mr. Dooley, "or be
wurruked."

THE GREAT HOT SPELL.

IT was sultry everywhere, but particularly in Archey Road; for in summer Archey Road is a tunnel for the south-west wind, which refreshes itself at the rolling-mill blasts, and spills its wrath upon the just and the unjust alike. Wherefore Mr. Dooley and Mr. McKenna were both steaming, as they sat at either side of the door of Mr. Dooley's place, with their chairs tilted back against the posts.

"Hot," said Mr. McKenna.

"Warrum," said Mr. Dooley.

"I think this is the hottest September that ever was," said Mr. McKenna.

"So ye say," said Mr. Dooley. "An' that's because ye're a young man, a kid. If ye was my age, ye'd know bether. How d'ye do, Mrs. Murphy? Go in, an' fill it ye'ersilf. Ye'll find th' funnel undher th' see-gar case.— Ye'd know bether thin that. Th' Siptimber iv th' year eighteen sixty-eight was so much hotter thin this that, if ye wint

fr'm wan to th' other, ye'd take noomoney
iv th' lungs,—ye wud so. 'Twas a remarkable summer, takin' it all in all. On th'
Foorth iv July they was a fut iv ice in
Haley's slough, an' I was near flooded out
be th' wather pipe bustin'. A man be th'
name iv Maloney froze his hand settin' off
a Roman candle near Main Sthreet, an'—
Tin cints, please, ma'am. Thank ye kindly.
How's th' good man?—As I said, it was a
remarkable summer. It rained all August,
an' th' boys wint about on rafts ; an' a sthreet-
car got lost fr'm th' road, an' I dhrove into
th' canal, an' all on boord— 'Avnin', Mike.
Ah-ha, 'twas a great fight. An' Buck got
his eye, did he ? A good man.

"Well, Jawn, along come Siptimber. It
begun fairly warrum, wan hundherd or so in
th' shade ; but no wan minded that. Thin
it got hotter an' hotter, an' people begun to
complain a little. They was sthrong in thim
days,— not like th' joods they raise now,—
an' a little heat more or less didn't kill thim.
But afther a while it was more thin most iv

thim wanted. The sthreet-car thracks got so soft they spread all over th' sthreet, an' th' river run dhry. Afther boilin' f'r five days like a — How are ye, Dempsey? Ye don't tell me? Now th' likes iv him runnin' f'r aldherman! I'd as lave vote f'r th' tillygraph pole. Well, be good to ye'ersilf. Folks all well? Thanks be.—They shut off th' furnaces out at th' mills, an' melted th' iron be puttin' it out in th' sun. Th' puddlers wurruked in iron cases, an' was kept alive be men playin' a hose on thim fr'm th' packin' house refrigerator. Wan iv thim poked his head out to light his pipe, an' he was — Well, well, Timothy, ye are quite a sthranger. Ah, dear oh me, that's too ba-ad, too ba-ad. I'll tell ye what ye do. Ye rub th' hand in half iv a potato, an' say tin pather an' avy's over it ivry day f'r tin days. 'Tis a sure cure. I had wan wanst. Th' kids are thrivin', I dinnaw? That's good. Betther to hear thim yellin' in th' sthreet thin th' sound iv th' docthor's gig at th' dure.

" Well, Jawn, things wint fr'm bad to worse. All th' beer in th' house was mulled; an' Mrs. Dinny Hogan — her that was Odelia O'Brien — burned her face atin' ice-crame down be th' Italyan man's place, on Halsthed Sthreet. 'Twas no sthrange sight to see an ice-wagon goin' along th' sthreet on fire — McCarthy! McCarthy! come over here! Sure, ye're gettin' proud, passin' by ye'er ol' frinds. How's thricks in th' Ninth? D'ye think he will? Well, I've heerd that, too; but they was a man in here to-day that says the Boohemians is out f'r him with axes. Good-night. Don't forget th' number.

" They was a man be th' name iv Daheny, Jawn, a cousin iv th' wan ye know, that started to walk up th' r-road fr'm th' bridge. Befure he got to Halsthed Sthreet, his shoes was on fire. He turned in an alarm; but th' fire departmint was all down on Mitchigan Avnoo, puttin' out th' lake, an'" —

" Putting out what?" demanded Mr. McKenna.

" Puttin' out th' lake," replied Mr.

Dooley, stolidly. "They was no insurance — A good avnin' to ye, Mrs. Doyle. Ye're goin' over, thin? I was there las' night, an' a finer wake I niver see. They do nawthin' be halves. How was himsilf? As natural as life? Yes, ma'am, rayqueem high mass, be carredges to Calv'ry.

"On th' twinty-fifth iv Siptimber a change come. It was very sudden; an', steppin' out iv th' ice-box where I slept in th' mornin', I got a chill. I wint for me flannels, an' stopped to look at th' thermomether. It was four hundherd an' sixty-five."

"How much?" asked Mr. McKenna.

"Four hundherd an' sixty-five."

"Fahrenheit?"

"No, it belonged to Dorsey. Ah! well, well, an' here's Cassidy. Come in, frind, an' have a shell iv beer. I've been tellin' Jawnny about th' big thaw iv eighteen sixty-eight. Feel th' wind, man alive. 'Tis turnin' cool, an' we'll sleep to-night."

KEEPING LENT.

Mr. McKenna had observed Mr. Dooley in the act of spinning a long, thin spoon in a compound which reeked pleasantly and smelt of the humming water of commerce; and he laughed and mocked at the philosopher.

"Ah-ha," he said, "that's th' way you keep Lent, is it? Two weeks from Ash Wednesday, and you tanking up."

Mr. Dooley went on deliberately to finish the experiment, leisurely dusting the surface with nutmeg and tasting the product before setting down the glass daintily. Then he folded his apron, and lay back in ample luxury while he began: "Jawn, th' holy season iv Lent was sent to us f'r to teach us th' weakness iv th' human flesh. Man proposes, an' th' Lord disposes, as Hinnissy says.

"I mind as well as though it was yesterday th' struggle iv me father f'r to keep Lent. He began to talk it a month befure th' time.

'On Ash Winsdah,' he'd say, 'I'll go in f'r a rale season iv fast an' abstinince,' he'd say. An' sure enough, whin Ash Winsdah come round at midnight, he'd take a long dhraw at his pipe an' knock th' ashes out slowly again his heel, an' thin put th' dhudeen up behind th' clock. 'There,' says he, 'there ye stay till Easter morn,' he says. Ash Winsdah he talked iv nawthin but th' pipe. ''Tis exthrordinney how easy it is f'r to lave off,' he says. 'All ye need is will power,' he says. 'I dinnaw that I'll iver put a pipe in me mouth again. 'Tis a bad habit, smokin' is,' he says; 'an' it costs money. A man's betther off without it. I find I dig twict as well,' he says; 'an', as f'r cuttin' turf, they'se not me like in th' parish since I left off th' pipe,' he says.

"Well, th' nex' day an' th' nex' day he talked th' same way; but Fridah he was sour, an' looked up at th' clock where th' pipe was. Saturdah me mother, thinkin' to be plazin to him, says: 'Terrence,' she says, 'ye're iver so much betther without th'

tobacco,' she says. 'I'm glad to find you
don't need it. Ye'll save money,' she says.
'Be quite, woman,' says he. 'Dear, oh
dear,' he says, 'I'd like a pull at th' clay,'
he says. 'Whin Easter comes, plaze Gawd,
I'll smoke mesilf black an' blue in th' face,'
he says.

"That was th' beginin' iv th' downfall.
Choosdah he was settin' in front iv th' fire
with a pipe in his mouth. 'Why, Terrence,'
says me mother, 'ye're smokin' again.'
'I'm not,' says he : ''tis a dhry smoke,' he
says ; ''tisn't lighted,' he says. Wan week
afther th' swear-off he came fr'm th' field
with th' pipe in his face, an' him puffin'
away like a chimney. 'Terrence,' says me
mother, 'it isn't Easter morn.' 'Ah-ho,'
says he, 'I know it,' he says ; 'but,' he says,
'what th' divvle do I care?' he says. 'I
wanted f'r to find out whether it had th'
masthery over me ; an',' he says, 'I've
proved that it hasn't,' he says. 'But what's
th' good iv swearin' off, if ye don't break
it?' he says. 'An' annyhow,' he says, 'I
glory in me shame.'

"Now, Jawn," Mr: Dooley went on, "I've got what Hogan calls a theery, an' it's this : that what's thrue iv wan man's thrue iv all men. I'm me father's son a'most to th' hour an' day. Put me in th' County Roscommon forty year ago, an' I'd done what he'd done. Put him on th' Ar-rchey Road, an' he'd be deliverin' ye a lecture on th' sin iv thinkin' ye're able to overcome th' pride iv th' flesh, as Father Kelly says. Two weeks ago I looked with contimpt on Hinnissy f'r an' because he'd not even promise to fast an' obstain fr'm croquet durin' Lent. To-night you see me mixin' me toddy without th' shadow iv re-morse about me. I'm proud iv it. An' why not? I was histin' in me first wan whin th' soggarth come down fr'm a sick call, an' looked in at me. 'In Lent?' he says, half-laughin' out in thim quare eyes iv his. 'Yes,' said I. 'Well,' he says, 'I'm not authorized to say this be th' propa-ganda,' he says, 'an' 'tis no part iv th' direc-tions f'r Lent,' he says; 'but,' he says, 'I'll

tell ye this, Martin,' he says, 'that they'se
more ways than wan iv keepin' th' season,'
he says. 'I've knowed thim that starved
th' stomach to feast th' evil temper,' he says.
'They'se a little priest down be th' Ninth
Ward that niver was known to keep a fast
day ; but Lent or Christmas tide, day in an'
day out, he goes to th' hospital where they
put th' people that has th' small-pox. Star-
vation don't always mean salvation. If it
did,' he says, 'they'd have to insure th'
pavemint in wan place, an' they'd be money
to burn in another. Not,' he says, 'that I
want ye to undherstand that I look kindly
on th' sin iv ' —

"'Tis a cold night out,' says I.

"'Well,' he says, th' dear man, 'ye may.
On'y,' he says, ''tis Lent.'

"'Yes,' says I.

"'Well, thin,' he says, 'by ye'er lave I'll
take but half a lump iv sugar in mine,' he
says."

THE QUICK AND THE DEAD.

Mr. Dooley and Mr. McKenna sat outside the ample door of the little liquor store, the evening being hot, and wrapped their legs around the chair, and their lips around two especially long and soothing drinks. They talked politics and religion, the people up and down the street, the chances of Murphy, the tinsmith, getting on the force, and a great deal about the weather. A woman in white started Mr. McKenna's nerves.

"Glory be, I thought it was a ghost!" said Mr. McKenna, whereupon the conversation drifted to those interesting phenomena. Mr. Dooley asked Mr. McKenna if he had ever seen one. Mr. McKenna replied that he hadn't, and didn't want to. Had Mr. Dooley? "No," said the philosopher, "I niver did; an' it's always been more thin sthrange to me that annywan shud come back afther he'd been stuck in a crate five feet deep, with a ton iv mud upon him.

'Tis onplisint iv thim, annyhow, not to say ongrateful. F'r mesilf, if I was wanst pushed off, an' they'd waked me kindly, an' had a solemn rayqueem high mass f'r me, an' a funeral with Roddey's Hi-beryan band, an' th' A-ho-aitches, I have too much pride to come back f'r an encore. I wud so, Jawn. Whin a man's dead, he ought to make th' best iv a bad job, an' not be thrapsin' around, lookin' f'r throuble among his own kind.

"No, I niver see wan, but I know there are such things; f'r twinty years ago all th' road was talkin' about how Flaherty, th' tailor, laid out th' ghost iv Tim O'Grady. O'Grady was a big sthrappin' Connock man, as wide across th' shoulders as a freight car. He was a plastherer be thrade whin wages was high, an' O'Grady was rowlin' in wealth. Ivry Sundah ye'd see him, with his horse an' buggy an' his goold watch an' chain, in front iv th' Sullivans' house, waitin' f'r Mary Ann Sullivan to go f'r a buggy ride with him over to McAllister Place; an' he

fin'lly married her, again th' wishes iv
Flaherty, who took to histin' in dhrinks, an'
missed his jooty, an' was a scandal in th'
parish f'r six months.

"O'Grady didn't improve with mathrimony, but got to lanin' again th' ol' stuff,
an' walkin' up an' down th' sidewalk in his
shirt-sleeves, with his thumbs stuck in his
vest, an' his little pipe turned upside down;
an', whin he see Flaherty, 'twas his custom
to run him up an alley, so that th' little
tailor man niver had a minyit iv peace.
Ivry wan supposed he lived in a three most
iv th' time, to be out iv th' way iv O'Grady.

"Well, wan day O'Grady he seen Flaherty
walkin' down th' sthreet with a pair iv lav-
ender pants f'r Willum Joyce to wear to th'
Ogden Grove picnic, an' thried to heave a
brick at him.   He lost his balance, an' fell
fr'm th' scaffoldin' he was wurrukin' on; an'
th' last wurruds he said was, 'Did I get
him or didn't I?'   Mrs. O'Grady said it
was th' will iv Gawd; an' he was burrid at
Calvary with a funeral iv eighty hacks, an'

a great manny people in their own buggies. Dorsey, th' conthractor, was there with his wife. He thought th' wurruld an' all iv O'Grady.

"Wan year aftherward Flaherty begun makin' up to Mrs. O'Grady; an' ivry wan in th' parish seen it, an' was glad iv it, an' said it was scandalous. How it iver got out to O'Grady's pew in th' burryin' ground, I'll niver tell ye, an' th' Lord knows; but wan evenin' th' ghost iv O'Grady come back. Flaherty was settin' in th' parlor, smokin' a seegar, with O'Grady's slippers on his feet, whin th' spook come in in th' mos' natural way in the wurruld, kickin' th' dog. 'What ar-re ye doin' here, ye little farryer iv pants?' he says. Mrs. O'Grady was f'r faintin'; but O'Flaherty he says, says he: 'Be quite,' he says. 'I'll dale with him.' Thin to th' ghost: 'Have ye paid th' rint here, ye big ape?' he says. 'What d'ye mane be comin' back, whin th' landlord ain't heerd fr'm ye f'r a year?' he says. Well, O'Grady's ghost was that sur-

prised he cud hardly speak. 'Ye ought to
have betther manners thin insultin' th' dead,'
he says. 'Ye ought to have betther manners thin to be lavin' ye'er coffin at this hour
iv th' night, an' breakin' in on dacint people,'
says Flaherty. 'What good does it do to
have rayqueem masses f'r th' raypose iv th'
like iv you,' he says, 'that doesn't know his
place?' he says. 'I'm masther iv this house,'
says th' ghost. 'Not on ye'er life,' says
Flaherty. 'Get out iv here, or I'll make
th' ghost iv a ghost out iv ye. I can lick
anny dead man that iver lived,' he said.

"With that th' ghost iv O'Grady made a
pass at him, an' they clinched an' rowled on
th' flure. Now a ghost is no aisy mark
f'r anny man, an' O'Grady's ghost was as
sthrong as a cow. It had Flaherty down on
th' flure an' was feedin' him with a book
they call th' 'Christyan Martyrs,' whin Mrs.
O'Grady put a bottle in Flaherty's hands.
'What's this?' says Flaherty. 'Howly
wather,' says Mrs. O'Grady. 'Sprinkle it
on him,' says Mrs. O'Grady. 'Woman,'

says th' tailor between th' chapter iv th' book, 'this is no time f'r miracles,' he says. An' he give O'Grady's ghost a treminjous wallop on th' head. Now, whether it was th' wather or th' wallop, I'll not tell ye; but, annyhow, th' ghost give wan yell an' disappeared. An' th' very next Sundah, whin Father Kelly wint into th' pulpit at th' gospel, he read th' names iv Roger Kickham Flaherty an' Mary Ann O'Grady."

"Did the ghost ever come back?" asked Mr. McKenna.

"Niver," said Mr. Dooley. "Wanst was enough. But, mind ye, I'd hate to have been wan iv th' other ghosts th' night O'Grady got home fr'm th' visit to O'Flaherty's. There might be ghosts that cud stand him off with th' gloves, but in a round an' tumble fight he cud lick a St. Patrick's Day procession iv thim."

THE SOFT SPOT.

"Anny more cyclone news?" Mr. Dooley asked Mr. McKenna, as he came in with a copy of an extra paper in his hand.

"Nothing much," Mr. McKenna responded. "This paper says the angel of death has give up riding on the whirlwind."

"Tis betther so," said Mr. Dooley: "a bicycle is more satisfactory f'r a steady thing. But, faith, 'tis no jokin' matter. May th' Lord forgive me f'r makin' light iv it! Jawn, whin I read about thim poor people down in St. Looey, sthruck be th' wrath iv Hivin' without more warnin' thin a man gets in a Polock church fight an' swept to their graves be th' hundhreds, me heart ached in me.

"But they'se always some compinsation in th' likes iv this. To see th' wurruld as it r-runs along in its ordinrey coorse, with ivry man seemin' to be lookin' f'r th' best iv it an' carryin' a little hammer f'r his fel-

low-suff'rers, ye'd think what Hinnissy calls
th' springs iv human sympathy was as dhry
in th' breast as a bricklayer's boot in a box
iv mortar. But let annything happen like
this, an' men ye'd suspect iv goin' round
with a cold chisel liftin' name-plates off iv
coffins comes to th' front with their lips full
iv comfort an' kindliness an', what's more to
th' point, their hands full iv coin.

"Years ago there used to be a man be th'
name iv O'Brien — no relation iv th' sinitor
— lived down be th' dumps. He was well
off, an' had quit wur-rkin' f'r a living.
Well, whether he'd been disappointed in
love or just naturally had a kick up to him
again th' wurruld I niver knew; but this
here ol' la-ad put in his time from morn till
night handin' out contimpt an' hathred to
all mankind. No wan was harder to rent
fr'm. He had some houses near Halsted
Sthreet, an' I've see him servin' five days'
notices on his tenants whin' th' weather was
that cold ye cudden't see th' inside iv th'
furnace-rooms at th' mill f'r th' frost on th'

window.   Of all th' landlords on earth,
th' Lord deliver me fr'm an' Irish wan.
Whether 'tis that fr'm niver holdin' anny
land in th' ol' counthry they put too high a
fondness on their places whin they get a lot
or two over here, I don't know; but they're
quicker with th' constable thin anny others.
I've seen men, that 'd divide their last cint
with ye pay night, as hard, whin it come to
gather in th' rent f'r two rooms in th' rear,
as if they was an Irish peer's agents; an'
O'Brien had no such start iv binivolence to
go on.   He niver seemed to pass th' poor-
box in church without wantin' to break into
it.   He charged cint per cint whin Casey, th'
plumber, buried his wife an' borrid money
f'r th' funeral expenses.   I see him wanst
chasin' th' agent iv th' Saint Vincent de
Pauls down th' road f'r darin' to ask him f'r
a contribution.   To look at his har-rsh red
face, as he sat at his window markin' up his
accounts, ye'd know he was hard in th' bit
an' heavy in th' hand.   An' so he was,— as
hard an' heavy as anny man I iver seen in
all me born days.

" Well, Peter O'Brien had lived on long enough to have th' pious curses iv th' entire parish, whin th' fire broke out, th' second fire iv sivinty-four, whin th' damage was tin or twinty millions iv dollars an' I lost a bull terrier be th' name iv Robert Immitt, r-runnin' afther th' ingines. O'Brien disappeared fr'm th' r-road durin' th' fire,— he had some property on th' South Side,— an' wasn't seen or heerd tell iv fr a day. Th' nex' mornin' th' rayport come in that he was seen walkin' over th' red bridge with a baby in his arms. ' Glory be!' says I: ' is th' man goin' to add canniballing to his other crimes?' Sure enough, as I sthud in th' dureway, along come O'Brien, with his hands scalded, his eyebrows gone, an' most iv his clothes tore fr'm his back, but silent an' grim as iver, with a mite iv a girl held tight to his breast, an' her fast asleep.

" He had a house back iv my place,— he ownded th' fifty feet frontin' on Grove Sthreet, bought it fr'm a man named Grogan, — an' 'twas rinted be a widdy lady be th'

name iv Sullivan, wife iv a bricklayer iv
th' same name. He was sthridin' into th'
Widow Sullivan's house; an' says he, 'Mis-
tress Sullivan,' he says. 'Yes,' says she, in
a thremble, knottin' her apron in her hands
an' standin' in front iv her own little wans,
'what can I do f'r ye?' she says. 'Th'
rent's not due till to-morrow.' 'I very well
know that,' he says; 'an' I want ye to take
care iv this wan', he says. 'An' I'll pay ye
f'r ye'er throuble,' he says.

"We niver knew where he got th' child:
he niver told annywan. Docthor Casey said
he was badly burnt about th' head an' hands.
He testified to it in a suit he brought again
O'Brien f'r curin' him. F'r th' man
O'Brien, instead iv rayformin' like they do
in th' play, was a long sight meaner afther
he done this wan thing thin iver befure. If
he was tight-fisted wanst, he was as close now
as calcimine on a rough-finished wall. He
put his tinints out in th' cold without
mercy, he kicked blind beggars fr'm th'
dure, an' on his dyin'-bed he come as near

bein' left be raison iv his thryin' to bargain
with th' good man f'r th' rayqueems as
annywan ye iver see. But he raised th'
little girl; an' I sometimes think that, whin
they count up th' cash, they'll let O'Brien
off with a character f'r that wan thing,
though there's some pretty hard tabs again
him.

"They ain't much point in what I've told
ye more thin this,— that beneath ivry man's
outside coat there lies some good feelin'.
We ain't as bad as we make ourselves out.
We've been stringin' ropes across th' sthreet
f'r th' people iv Saint Looey f'r thirty years
an' handin' thim bricks fr'm th' chimbleys
whiniver we got a chance, but we've on'y
got wurruds an' loose change f'r thim whin
th' hard times comes."

"Yes," said Mr. McKenna, "I see even
the aldhermen has come to the front, offering
relief."

"Well," said Mr. Dooley, thoughtfully,
"I on'y hope they won't go to Saint Looey
to disthri-bute it thimsilves. That would
be a long sight worse thin th' cyclone."

THE IRISHMAN ABROAD.

MR. DOOLEY laid down his morning paper, and looked thoughtfully at the chandeliers.

"Taaffe," he said musingly,— "Taaffe — where th' divvle? Th' name's familiar."

"He lives in the Nineteenth," said Mr. McKenna. "If I remember right, he has a boy on th' force."

"Goowan," said Mr. Dooley, "with ye'er nineteenth wa-ards. Th' Taaffe I mane is in Austhria. Where in all, where in all? No: yes, by gar, I have it. A-ha!

> " But cur-rsed be th' day,
>> Whin Lord Taaffe grew faint-hearted
>> An' sthud not n'r cha-arged,
>> But in panic depa-arted."

"D'ye mind it,— th' pome by Joyce? No, not Bill Joyce. Joyce, th' Irish pote that wrote th' pome about th' wa-ars whin me people raysisted Cromwell, while yours was carryin' turf on their backs to make fires for th' crool invader, as Finerty says whin th' sub-scriptions r-runs low. 'Tis th' same name, a good ol' Meath name in th' days gone by; an' be th' same token I have in me head that this here Count Taaffe, whether he's an austrich or a canary bur-rd now, is wan iv th' ol' fam'ly. There's manny iv thim in Europe an' all th' wurruld beside. There was Pat McMahon, th' Frinchman, that bate Looey Napoleon; an' O'Donnell, the Spanish juke; an' O'Dhriscoll an' Lynch, who do be th' whole thing down be South America, not to mention Patsy Bolivar. Ye can't go annywhere fr'm Sweden to Boolgahria without findin' a Turk settin' up beside th' king an' dalin' out th' deek with his own hand. Jawn, our people makes poor Irishmen, but good Dutchmen; an', th' more I see iv thim, th' more I says to mesilf that th' rale boney fide Irishman is no more thin a foreigner born away from home. 'Tis so.

"Look at thim, Jawn," continued Mr. Dooley, becoming eloquent. "Whin there's

battles to be won, who do they sind for?
McMahon or Shurdan or Phil Kearney or
Colonel Colby. Whin there's books to be
wrote, who writes thim but Char-les Lever
or Oliver Goldsmith or Willum Carleton?
Whin there's speeches to be made, who
makes thim but Edmund Burke or Macchew
P. Brady? There's not a land on th' face
iv th' wurruld but th' wan where an Irishman doesn't stand with his fellow-man, or
above thim. Whin th' King iv Siam wants
a plisint evenin', who does he sind f'r but a
lively Kerry man that can sing a song or
play a good hand at spile-five? Whin th'
Sultan iv Boolgahria takes tea, 'tis tin to wan
th' man across fr'm him is more to home in
a caubeen thin in a turban. There's Mac's
an' O's in ivry capital iv Europe atin' off
silver plates whin their relations is staggerin'
under th' creels iv turf in th' Connaught
bogs.

"Wirra, 'tis hard. Ye'd sa-ay off hand,
'Why don't they do as much for their own
counthry?' Light-spoken are thim that sug-

gests th' like iv that. 'Tis asier said than done. Ye can't grow flowers in a granite block, Jawn dear, much less whin th' first shoot 'd be thrampled under foot without pity. 'Tis aisy f'r us over here, with our bellies full, to talk iv th' cowardice iv th' Irish; but what would ye have wan man iv thim do again a rig'ment? 'Tis little fightin' th' lad will want that will have to be up before sunrise to keep th' smoke curlin' fr'm th' chimbley or to patch th' rush roof to keep out th' March rain. No, faith, Jawn, there's no soil in Ireland f'r th' greatness iv th' race; an' there has been none since th' wild geese wint across th' say to France, hangin' like flies to th' side iv th' Fr-rinch ship. 'Tis only f'r women an' childher now, an' thim that can't get away. Will th' good days ever come again? says ye. Who knows!"

THE SERENADE.

"By dad, if it wasn't f'r that there Molly Donahue," said Mr. Dooley to Mr. Mc-Kenna, "half th' life 'd be gone out iv Bridgeport." "What has Molly Donahue been doin'?" asked Mr. McKenna.

"She have been causin' Felix Pindergasht to be sint to th' Sisters iv Mercy Hospital with inflammathry rhoomatism. Ye know Felix. He is a musical janius. Befure he was tin year old he had me mind disthracted be playin' wan iv thim little mouth organs on th' corner near me bedroom window. Thin he larned to play th' ack-carjeen, an' cud swing it between his legs an' give an imitation iv th' cathedral bell that 'd make ye dig in ye'er pocket to see iv ye had a dime f'r a seat. Thin he used to sit in his window in his shirt-sleeves, blowin' 'Th' Vale iv Avoca' on a cornet. He was wan whole month befure he cud get th' 'shall fade fr'm me heart' right. Half th' neighborhood 'd be out on th' sidewalk yellin'

' Lift it, Felix,— lift an' scatther it. Shall
fade fr'm me ha-a-rt,— lift it, ye clumsy
piper.'

"A few months back th' stupid gawk
begun to be attintive to Molly Donahue, an',
like th' wild wan she is, she dhrew him on.
Did ye iver see th' wan that wudden't?
Faith, they're all alike. If it ain't a sthraight
stick, it's a crooked wan; an' th' man was
niver yet born, if he had a hump on his
back as big as coal-scuttle an' had a face like
th' back iv a hack, that cudden't get th' wink
iv th' eye fr'm some woman. They're all
alike, all alike. Not that I've annything
again thim: 'tis thim that divides our sorrows
an' doubles our joys, an' sews chiny buttons
on our pa-ants an' mends our shirts with
blue yarn. But they'll lead a man to desthruction an' back again, thim same women.

"Well, Felix had no luck coortin' Molly
Donahue. Wan night she wasn't in; an th'
nex' night ol' man Donahue come to th'
dure, an' says, ' Ye can put in th' coal at th'
back dure,' he says, an' near broke th' la-ad's

heart. Las' week he pulled himself together, an' wint up th' r-road again. He took his cornet with him in a green bag; an', whin he got in front iv Donahue's house, he outs with th' horn, an' begins to play. Well, sir, at th' first note half th' block was in th' sthreet. Women come fr'm their houses, with their shawls on their heads; an' all th' forty-fives games was broke up be raison iv th' la-ads lavin' f'r to hear the music. Be-fure Felix had got fairly started f'r to serry-nade Molly Donahue, th' crowd was big an' boistherous. He started on th' ol' favor-ite, ' Th' Vale iv Avoca '; an' near ivry man in th' crowd had heerd him practisin' it. He wint along splendid till he come to 'shall fade fr'm me heart,' an' thin he broke. ' Thry again,' says th' crowd; an' he stharted over. He done no betther on th' second whirl. ' Niver say die, Felix,' says th' crowd. ' Go afther it. We're all with ye.' At that th' poor, deluded loon tackled it again; an' th' crowd yells: ' Hist it up. There ye go. No, be hivins he fell at th' last jump.' An', by dad, though he thried f'r half an hour, he cud not land th' 'shall fade fr'm me heart.' At th' last break th' light in Molly Donahue's window wint out, an' th' crowd dispersed. Felix was discons'-late. 'I had it right befure I come up,' he says, 'but I missed me holt whin th' crowd come. Me heart's broke,' he says. 'Th' cornet's not ye'er insthrument,' says Dorsey. 'Ye shud thry to play th' base dhrum. It's asier.' "

" Is that all that's going on?" asked Mr. McKenna.

" That an' th' death iv wan iv Hinnissy's goats,— Marguerite. No, no, not that wan. That's Odalia. Th' wan with th' brown spots. That's her. She thried to ate wan iv thim new theayter posthers, an' perished in great ag'ny. They say th' corpse turned red at th' wake, but ye can't believe all ye hear."

THE HAY FLEET.

MR. DOOLEY had been reading about General Shafter's unfortunately abandoned enterprise for capturing Santiago by means of a load of hay, and it filled him with great enthusiasm. Laying down his paper, he said: " By dad, I always said they give me frind Shafter th' worst iv it. If they'd left him do th' job th' way he wanted to do it, he'd 've taken Sandago without losin' an ounce."

" How was it he wanted to do it? " Mr. Hennessy asked.

" Well," said Mr. Dooley, " 'twas this way. This is th' way it was. Ol' Cervera's fleet was in th' harbor an' bottled up, as th' man says. Shafter he says to Sampson: ' Look here, me bucko, what th' divvle ar-re ye loafin' ar-round out there f'r,' he says, ' like a dep'ty sheriff at a prize fight?' he says. ' Why don't ye go in, an' smash th' Castiles?' he says. ' I'm doin' well where I am,' says Sampson. ' Th' navy iv th'

United States,' he says, 'which is wan iv th'
best, if not th' best, in th' wurruld,' he says,
'was not,' he says, 'intinded f'r sthreet
fightin',' he says. 'We'll stay here,' he
says, 'where we ar-re,' he says, 'until,' he
says, 'we can equip th' ships with noomatic
tire wheels,' he says, 'an' ball bearin's,' he
says.

"'Well,' says Shafter, 'if ye won't go in,'
he says, 'we'll show ye th' way,' he says.
An' he calls on Cap Brice, that was wan iv
th' youngest an' tastiest dhressers in th'
whole crool an' devastatin' war. 'Cap,' he
says, 'is they anny hay in th' camp?' he
says. 'Slathers iv it,' says th' cap. 'Onless,' he says, 'th' sojers et it,' he says.
'Th' las' load iv beef that come down fr'm
th' undhertakers,' he says, 'was not good,'
he says. 'Ayether,' he says, ''twas im-
properly waked,' he says, 'or,' he says, 'th'
pall-bearers was careless,' he says. 'Annyhow,' he says, 'th' sojers won't eat it; an',
whin I left, they was lookin' greedily at th'
hay,' he says. 'Cap,' says Gin'ral Shafter,

'if anny man ates a wisp, shoot him on th'
spot,' he says. 'Those hungry sojers may
desthroy me hopes iv victhry,' he says.
'What d'ye mane?' says Cap Brice. 'I
mane this,' says Gin'ral Shafter. 'I mane
to take yon fortress,' he says. 'I'll sind ye
in, Cap,' he says, 'in a ship protected be
hay,' he says. 'Her turrets 'll be alfalfa,
she'll have three inches iv solid timithy to
th' water line, an' wan inch iv th' best clover
below th' wather line,' he says. 'Did ye
iver see an eight-inch shell pinithrate a bale
iv hay?' he says. 'I niver did,' says Cap
Brice. 'Maybe that was because I niver see
it thried,' he says. 'Be that as it may,' says
Gin'ral Shafter, 'ye niver see it done. No
more did I,' he says. 'Onless,' he says,
'they shoot pitchforks,' he says, 'they'll
niver hur-rt ye,' he says. 'Ye'll be onvin-
cible,' he says. 'Ye'll pro-ceed into th'
harbor,' he says, 'behind th' sturdy armor
iv projuce,' he says. 'Let ye'er watchword
be "Stay on th' far-rm," an' go on to
victhry,' he says. 'Gin'ral,' says Cap Brice,

'how can I thank ye f'r th' honor?' he says.
''Tis no wondher th' men call ye their
fodder,' he says. 'Twas a joke Cap Brice
med at th' time. 'I'll do th' best I can,'
he says; 'an', if I die in th' attempt,' he says,
'bury me where the bran-mash 'll wave over
me grave,' he says.

"An' Gin'ral Shafter he got together his
fleet, an' put th' armor on it. 'Twas a
formidable sight. They was th' cruiser
'Box Stall,' full armored with sixty-eight
bales iv th' finest grade iv chopped feed; th'
'R-red Barn,' a modhern hay battleship, protected be a whole mow iv timothy; an' th'
gallant little 'Haycock,' a torpedo boat
shootin' deadly missiles iv explosive oats.
Th' expedition was delayed be wan iv th'
mules sthrollin' down to th' shore an' atin' up
th' afther batthry an' par-rt iv th' ram iv th'
'R-red Barn' an', befure repairs was made,
Admiral Cervera heerd iv what was goin' on.
'Glory be to the saints,' he says, 'what an in-
jaynious thribe these Yankees is!' says he.
'On'y a few weeks ago they thried to de-

sthroy me be dumpin' a load iv coal on me,'
he says; 'an' now,' he says, 'they're goin'
to smother me in feed,' he says. 'They'll
be rollin' bar'ls iv flour on me fr'm th' heights
next,' he says. 'I'd betther get out,' he says.
''Tis far nobler,' he says, 'to purrish on th'
ragin' main,' he says, 'thin to die with
ye'er lungs full iv hayseed an' ye'er eyes
full iv dust,' he says. 'I was born in a large
city,' he says; 'an' I don't know th' rules iv
th' barn,' he says. An' he wint out, an' took
his lickin'.

" 'Twas too bad Shafter didn't get a chanst
at him, but he's give th' tip to th' la-ads
that makes th' boats. No more ixpinsive
steel an' ir'n, but good ol' grass fr'm th'
twinty-acre meadow. Th' ship-yards 'll be
moved fr'm th' say, an' laid down in th'
neighborhood iv Polo, Illinye, an' all th'
Mississippi Valley'll ring with th' sound iv
th' scythe an' th' pitchfork buildin' th' definse iv our counthry's honor. Thank th'
Lord, we've winrows an' winrows iv Shafter's armor plate between here an' Dubuque."

Mr. Hennessy said good-night. "As me cousin used to say," he remarked, "we're through with wan hell iv a bad year, an' here goes f'r another like it."

"Well," said Mr. Dooley, "may th' Lord niver sind us a foolisher wan than this!"

THE PERFORMANCES OF
LIEUTENANT HOBSON.

"If I'd been down to th' Audjitooroom th' other night," said Mr. Hennessy, "an' had a chunk iv coal fr'm th' sunk ' Merrimac,' I'd iv handed it to that man Loot Hobson. I wud so. Th' idee iv a hero standin' up befure thousan's iv men with fam'lies an' bein' assaulted be ondacint females. It med me blush down to th' soles iv me feet. If they let this thing go on, be hivins, why do they stop th' hootchy-kootchy?"

"Ividinces iv affection is always odjious to an Irishman," said Mr. Dooley, "an' to all reel affectionate people. But me frind Hobson's not to blame. 'Tis th' way th' good Lord has iv makin' us cow'rds con- tinted with our lot that he niver med a brave man yet that wasn't half a fool. I've more sinse an' wisdom in th' back iv me thumb thin all th' heroes in th' wurruld. That's why I ain't a hero. If Hobson had intilli- gence, he'd be wurrukin' in th' post-office;

an', if anny ol' hin thried to kiss him, he 'd
call f'r th' polis.   Bein' young an' foolish,
whin me frind Sampson says, ' Is there anny
man here that 'll take this ol' coal barge in
beyant an' sink it, an' save us th' throuble iv
dhrownin' on our way home?' Loot Hobson says, says he : ' Here I am, Cap,' says
he.   ' I'll take it in,' he says, ' an' seal up
th' hated Castiles,' he says, ' so that they can
niver get out,' he says.   ' But,' he says, ' I'll
lave a hole f'r thim to get out whin they
want to get out,' he says.   An' he tuk some
other la-ads,— I f'rget their names,— they
wasn't heroes, annyhow, but was wurrukin'
be th' day ; an' he wint in in his undherclothes, so's not to spoil his suit, an' th' Castiles hurled death an' desthruction on him.
An' it niver touched him no more thin it did
anny wan else ; an' thin they riscued him fr'm
himsilf, an' locked him up in th' polis station an' fed him th' best they knew how.   An'
he wint on a lecther tour, an' here he is.   Be
hivins, I think he's more iv a hero now thin
iver he was.   I'd stand up befure a cross-

eyed Spanish gunner an' take his shootin'
without a mask mesilf; but I'd shy hard if
anny ol' heifer come up, an' thried to kiss
me.

"On th' flure iv th' 'Merrimac,' in his
light undherclothes, Loot Hobson was a
sthrong, foolish man. On th' stage iv th'
Audjitooroom, bein' caressed be women
that 'd kiss th' Indyun in front iv a see-gar
sthore, if he didn't carry a tommyhawk, he's
still foolish, but not sthrong.   'Tis so with all
heroes. Napolyeon Bonyparte, th' Impror
iv th' Fr-rinch, had manny carryin's on, I've
heerd tell; an' ivry man knows that, whin
Jawn Sullivan wasn't in th' r-ring, he was no
incyclopedja f'r intilligence. No wan thried
to kiss him, though. They knew betther.

"An' Hobson 'll larn. He's young yet,
th' Loot is; an' he's goin' out to th' Ph'lippeens to wurruk f'r Cousin George. Cousin
George is no hero, an' 'tisn't on record that
anny wan iver thried to scandalize his good
name be kissin' him. I'd as lave, if I was
a foolish woman, which, thanks be, I'm not,

hug a whitehead torpedo as Cousin George.
He'll be settin' up on th' roof iv his boat,
smokin' a good see-gar, an' wondhrin' how
manny iv th' babbies named afther him 'll
be in th' pinitinchry be th' time he gets back
home.   Up comes me br-rave Hobson.
'Who ar-re ye, disturbin' me quite?' says
Cousin George. 'I'm a hero,' says th' Loot.
'Ar-re ye, faith?' says Cousin George.
'Well,' he says, 'I can't do annything f'r ye
in that line,' he says.   'All th' hero jobs on
this boat,' he says, 'is compitintly filled,' he
says, 'be mesilf,' he says.   'I like to see th'
wurruk well done,' he says, 'so,' he says, 'I
don't thrust it to anny wan,' he says.   'With
th' aid iv a small boy, who can shovel more
love letthers an' pothry overboard thin anny
wan I iver see,' he says, 'I'm able to clane
up me hero business befure noon ivry day,'
he says.   'What's ye'er name?' he says.
'Hobson,' says th' loot.   'Niver heerd iv
ye, says Cousin George.   'Where'd ye
wurruk last?' 'Why,' says th' Loot, 'I'm
th' man that sunk th' ship,' he says; 'an'

I've been kissed be hundherds iv women at home,' he says. ' Is that so?' says Cousin George. ' Well, I don't b'lieve in sinkin' me own ship,' he says. ' Whin I'm lookin' f'r a divarsion iv that kind, I sink somebody else's,' he says. ' 'Tis cheaper. As f'r th' other thing,' he says, ' th' less ye say about that, th' betther,' he says. ' If some iv these beauchious Ph'lippeen belles ar-round here hears,' he says, 'that ye're in that line, they may call on ye to give ye a chaste salute,' he says, ' an',' he says, ' f'rget,' he says, ' to take th' see-gars out iv their mouths,' he says. ' Ye desthroyed a lot iv coal, ye tell me,' he says. ' Do ye,' he says, ' go downstairs now, an' shovel up a ton or two iv it,' he says. ' Afther which,' he says, ' ye can roll a kag iv beer into me bedroom,' he says; ' f'r 'tis dhry wurruk settin' up here watchin' ixpansion ixpand,' he says.

" That's what Cousin George'll say to th' Loot. An', whin th' Loot comes back, he won't be a hero anny more; an', if anny woman thries to kiss him, he'll climb a

three.   Cousin George'll make a man iv
him.   'Tis kicks, not kisses, that makes men
iv heroes."

"Well, mebbe ye're r-right," said Mr.
Hennessy.   "He's nawthin' but a kid, annyhow,— no oldher thin me oldest boy; an'
I know what a fool he'd be if anny wan ast
him to be more iv a fool thin he is.   Hobson 'll be famous, no matther what foolish
things he does."

"I dinnaw," said Mr. Dooley.   "It was
headed f'r him; but I'm afraid, as th' bull-
yard players 'd say, fame's been kissed
off."

THE DECLINE OF NATIONAL
FEELING.

"WHAT ar-re ye goin' to do Patrick's Day?" asked Mr. Hennessy.

"Patrick's Day?" said Mr. Dooley. "Patrick's Day? It seems to me I've heard th' name befure. Oh, ye mane th' day th' low Irish that hasn't anny votes cillybrates th' birth iv their naytional saint, who was a Fr-rinchman."

"Ye know what I mane," said Mr. Hennessy, with rising wrath. "Don't ye get gay with me now."

"Well," said Mr. Dooley, "I may cillybrate it an' I may not. I'm thinkin' iv savin' me enthusyasm f'r th' queen's birthday, whiniver it is that that blessid holiday comes ar-round. Ye see, Hinnissy, Patrick's Day is out iv fashion now. A few years ago ye'd see the Prisident iv th' United States marchin' down Pinnsylvanya Avnoo, with the green scarf iv th' Ancient Ordher on his shoulders an' a shamrock in his hat.

Now what is Mack doin'? He's settin' in
his parlor, writin' letthers to th' queen, be
hivins, askin' afther her health. He was
fr'm th' north iv Ireland two years ago, an'
not so far north ayether,—just far enough
north f'r to be on good terms with Derry
an' not far enough to be bad frinds with
Limerick. He was raised on butthermilk
an' haggis, an' he dhrank his Irish nate with
a dash iv orange bitthers in it. He's been
movin' steadily north since ; an', if he keeps
on movin', he'll go r-round th' globe, an'
bring up somewhere in th' south iv England.

"An' Hinnery Cabin Lodge! I used to
think that Hinnery would niver die con-
tint till he'd took th' Prince iv Wales be th'
hair iv th' head,— an' 'tis little th' poor
man's got,— an' dhrag him fr'm th' tower iv
London to Kilmainham Jail, an' hand him
over to th' tindher mercies, as Hogan says,
iv Michael Davitt. Thim was th' days
whin ye'd hear Hinnery in th' Sinit, spread-
in' fear to th' hear-rts iv th' British aristoc-
racy. 'Gintlemen,' he says, 'an' fellow-

sinitors, th' time has come,' he says, 'whin th' eagle burrud iv freedom,' he says, 'lavin',' he says, 'its home in th' mountains,' he says, 'an' circlin',' he says, 'undher th' jool'd hivin,' he says, 'fr'm where,' he says, 'th' Passamaquoddy rushes into Lake Erastus K. Ropes,' he says, 'to where rowls th' Oregon,' he says, 'fr'm th' lakes to th' gulf,' he says, 'fr'm th' Atlantic to th' Passific where rowls th' Oregon,' he says, 'an' fr'm ivry American who has th' blood iv his ancesthors' hathred iv tyranny in his veins,— your ancesthors an' mine, Mr. McAdoo,' he says, —'there goes up a mute prayer that th' nation as wan man, fr'm Bangor, Maine, to where rowls th' Oregon, that,' he says, 'is full iv salmon, which is later put up in cans, but has th' same inthrest as all others in this question,' he says, 'that,' he says, 'th' descindants iv Wash'nton an',' he says, 'iv Immitt,' he says, 'will jine hands f'r to protect,' he says, 'th' codfisheries again th' Vandal hand iv th' British line,' he says. 'I therefore move ye, Mr. Prisident, that it is

th' sinse iv this house, if anny such there
be, that Tay Pay O'Connor is a greater
man thin Lord Salisberry,' he says.

"Now where's Hinnery? Where's th'
bould Fenian? Where's th' moonlighter?
Where's th' pikeman? Faith, he's changed
his chune, an' 'tis 'Sthrangers wanst, but
brothers now,' with him, an' 'Hands acrost
th' sea an' into some wan's pocket,' an'
'Take up th' white man's burden an' hand
it to th' coons,' an' 'An open back dure an' a
closed fr-ront dure.' 'Tis th' same with all
iv thim. They'se me frind Joe Choate.
Where'd Joe spind th' night? Whisper, in
Windsor Castle, no less, in a night-shirt iv
th' Prince iv Wales; an' the nex' mornin',
whin he come downstairs, they tol' him th'
rile fam'ly was late risers, but, if he wanted
a good time, he cud go down an' look at th'
cimit'ry! An' he done it. He went out
an' wept over th' grave iv th' Father iv his
Counthry. Ye'er man, George Washington,
Hinnissy, was on'y th' stepfather.

"Well, glory be, th' times has changed

since me frind Jawn Finerty come out iv th'
House iv Riprisintatives; an', whin some
wan ast him what was goin' on, he says,
' Oh, nawthin' at all but some damned American business.' Thim was th' days! An'
what's changed thim? Well, I might be
sayin' 'twas like wanst whin me cousin Mike
an' a Kerry man be th' name iv Sullivan had
a gredge again a man named Doherty, that
was half a Kerry man himsilf. They kept
Doherty indures f'r a day, but by an' by
me cousin Mike lost inthrest in th' gredge,
havin' others that was newer, an' he wint
over to th' ya-ards; an' Doherty an' Sullivan begin to bow to each other, an' afther a
while they found that they were blood relations, an', what's closer thin that whin ye're
away fr'm home, townies. An' they hooked
arms, an' sthrutted up an' down th' road,
as proud as imprors. An' says they, ' We
can lick annything in th' ward,' says they.
But, befure they injyed th' 'lieance f'r long,
around th' corner comes me cousin Mike,
with a half-brick in each hand; an' me

brave Sullivan gives Doherty th' Kerry man's thrip, an' says he, 'Mike,' he says, 'I was on'y pullin' him on to give ye a crack at him,' he says. An' they desthroyed Doherty, so that he was in bed f'r a week."

"Well, I wondher will Mike come back?" said Mr. Hennessy.

"Me cousin Mike," said Mr. Dooley, "niver missed an iliction. An' whin th' campaign opened, there wasn't a man on th' ticket, fr'm mayor to constable, that didn't claim him f'r a first cousin. There are different kinds iv hands from acrost th' sea. There are pothry hands an' rollin'-mill hands; but on'y wan kind has votes."

"CYRANO DE BERGERAC."

"Ivry winter Hogan's la-ad gives a show
with what he calls th' Sixth Wa-ard Shakspere an' Willum J. Bryan Club, an' I was
sayjooced into goin' to wan las' night at
Finucane's hall," said Mr. Dooley.

"Th' girls was goin'," said Mr. Hennessy;
"but th' sthovepipe come down on th'
pianny, an' we had a minsthrel show iv our
own. What was it about, I dinnaw?"

"Well, sir," said Mr. Dooley, "I ain't
much on th' theayter. I niver wint to wan
that I didn't have to stand where I cud see
a man in blue overalls scratchin' his leg just
beyant where the heeroyne was prayin' on
th' palace stairs, an' I don't know much
about it; but it seemed to me, an' it seemed
to Hartigan, th' plumber, that was with me,
that 'twas a good play if they'd been a fire
in th' first act. They was a lot iv people
there; an', if it cud 've been arranged f'r to
have injine company fifteen with Cap'n
Duffy at th' head iv thim come in through

a window an' carry off th' crowd, 'twud 've
med a hit with me.

" 'Tis not like anny play I iver see befure
or since. In 'Tur-rble Tom; or, th' Boys
iv Ninety-eight,' that I see wanst, th' man
that's th' main guy iv th' thing he waits till
ivry wan has said what he has to say, an' he
has a clean field; an' thin he jumps in as th'
man that plays th' big dhrum gives it an
upper cut. But with this here play iv 'Cyrus
O'Bergerac' 'tis far diff'rent. Th' curtain
goes up an' shows Bill Delaney an' little
Tim Scanlan an' Mark Toolan an' Packy
Dugan, that wurruks in the shoe store, an'
Molly Donahue an' th' Casey sisters, thim
that scandalized th' parish be doin' a skirt
dance at th' fair, all walkin' up an' down
talkin'. 'Tin to wan on Sharkey,' says
Toolan. 'I go ye, an' make it a hundherd,'
says Tim Scanlan. 'Was ye at th' cake
walk?' 'Who stole me hat?' 'Cudden't
ye die waltzin'?' 'They say Murphy has
gone on th' foorce.' 'Hivins, there goes th'
las' car!' 'Pass th' butther, please: I'm far

fr'm home.' All iv thim talkin' away at once, niver carin' f'r no wan, whin all at wanst up stheps me bold Hogan with a nose on him,— glory be, such a nose! I niver see th' like on a man or an illyphant.

"Well, sir, Hogan is Cy in th' play; an' th' beak is pa-art iv him. What does he do? He goes up to Toolan, an' says he: 'Ye don't like me nose. It's an ilicthric light globe. Blow it out. It's a Swiss cheese. Cut it off, if ye want to. It's a brick in a hat. Kick it. It's a balloon. Hang a basket on it, an' we'll have an' ascinsion. It's a dure-bell knob. Ring it. It's a punchin' bag. Hit it, if ye dahr. F'r two pins I'd push in th' face iv ye.' An', mind ye, Hinnissy, Toolan had said not wan wurrud about th' beak,— not wan wurrud. An' ivry wan in th' house was talkin' about it, an' wondhrin' whin it'd come off an' smash somewan's fut. I looked f'r a fight there an' thin. But Toolan's a poor-spirited thing, an' he wint away. At that up comes Scanlan; an' says he: 'Look here, young fellow,' he says, 'don't get gay,' he says, 'don't get gay,' he says. 'What's that?' says Hogan. Whin a man says, 'What's that?' in a bar-room, it manes a fight, if he says it wanst. If he says it twict, it manes a fut race. 'I say,' says Scanlan, 'that, if ye make anny more funny cracks, I'll hitch a horse to that basket fender,' he says, 'an' dhrag it fr'm ye,' he says. At that Hogan dhrew his soord, an' says he : 'Come on,' he says, 'come on, an' take a lickin,' he says. An' Scanlan dhrew his soord, too. 'Wait,' says Hogan. 'Wait a minyit,' he says. 'I must think,' he says. 'I must think a pome,' he says. 'Whiniver I fight,' he says, 'I always have a pome,' he says. 'Glory be,' says I, 'there's Scanlan's chanst to give it to him,' I says. But Scanlan was as slow as a dhray ; an', befure he cud get action, Hogan was at him, l'adin' with th' pome an' counthrin' with the soord. 'I'll call this pome,' he says, 'a pome about a gazabo I wanst had a dool with in Finucane's hall,' he says. 'I'll threat ye r-right,'

he says, 'an' at the last line I'll hand ye
wan,' he says. An' he done it. 'Go in,'
he says in th' pome, 'go in an do ye'er
worst,' he says. 'I make a pass at ye'er
stomach,' he says, 'I cross ye with me
right,' he says; 'an,' he says at th' last line,
he says, 'I soak ye,' he says. An' he done
it. Th' minyit 'twas over with th' pome
'twas off with Scanlan. Th' soord wint into
him, an' he sunk down to th' flure; an' they
had to carry him off. Well, sir, Hogan was
that proud ye cudden't hold him f'r th'
rest iv th' night. He wint around ivrywhere stickin' people an' soakin' thim with
pothry. He's a gr-reat pote is this here
Hogan, an' a gr-reat fighter. He done thim
all at both; but, like me ol' frind Jawn L., he
come to th' end. A man dhropped a two-
be-four on his head wan day, an' he died.
Honoria Casey was with him as he passed
away, an' she says, 'How d'ye feel?' 'All
right,' says Hogan. 'But wan thing I'll
tell ye has made life worth livin',' he says.
'What's that?' says Miss Casey. 'I know,'

CYRANO DE BERGERAC" 233

says I. ' Annywan cud guess it. He manes
his nose,' I says. But ivrywan on th' stage
give it up. ' Ye don't know,' says Hogan.
' 'Tis me hat,' he says ; an', makin a low bow
to th' audjence, he fell to th' flure so hard
that his nose fell off an' rowled down on
Mike Finnegan. ' I don't like th' play,'
says Finnegan, ' an' I'll break ye'er nose,' he
says ; an' he done it. He's a wild divvle.
Hogan thried to rayturn th' compliment on
th' sidewalk afterward ; but he cudden't think
iv a pome, an' Finnegan done him."

"Well, said Mr. Hennessy, "I'd like
to've been there to see th' fightin'."

"In th' play ? " asked Mr. Dooley.

"No," said Mr. Hennessy. "On th'
sidewalk."

THE UNION OF TWO GREAT
FORTUNES.

"THEY'SE wan thing that always makes me feel sure iv what Hogan calls th' safety iv our dimmycratic institutions," said Mr. Dooley, "an' that's th' intherest th' good people iv New York takes in a weddin' iv th' millyionaires. Anny time a millyionaire condiscinds to enther th' martial state, as Hogan says, an', as Hogan says, make vows to Hyman, which is the Jew god iv marredge, he can fill th' house an' turn people away fr'm th' dure. An' he does. Th' sthreets is crowded. Th' cars can har'ly get through. Th' polis foorce is out, an' hammerin' th' heads iv th' delighted throng. Riprisintatives iv th' free an' inlightened press, th' pollutyem iv our liberties, as Hogan says, bright, intilligent young journalists, iver ready to probe fraud an' sham, disgeesed as waithers, is dashin' madly about, makin' notes on their cuffs. Business is suspinded. They'se no money in Wall Sthreet. It's all

at th' sacred scene. Hour be hour, as th'
prisints ar-re delivered, th' bank rates go up.
Th' Threeasury Departmint has to go on a
silver basis, there bein' no goold to manny-
facther into plunks.

"Inside th' house th' prisints cast a
goolden gleam on th' beauchious scene. Th'
happy father is seen seated at a table, dictat-
tin' millyion-dollar checks to a stinographer.
Th' goold chandeliers is draped with r-ropes
iv dimon's an' pearls. Th' hired girl is
passin' dhrinks in goolden goblets. Twinty
firemen fr'm th' New York Cinthral Railroad
is shovellin' di'mon'-studded pickle crutes
into th' back yard, among th' yachts an'
horses. Chansy Depoo enthers an' thrips
over a box iv bonds. 'Ar-re these th' holy
bonds iv mathrimony?' he says; f'r he is a
wild divvle, an' ye can't stop his jokin', avin
on solemn occasions.

"Th' soggarth comes in afther a while,
carryin' a goold prayer-book, th' gift iv th'
Rothscheelds, an' stands behind a small but
valyable pree Doo. To th' soft, meelojous

chune iv th' Wagner Palace Weddin' March fr'm ' Long Green,' th' groom enthers, simply but ixpinsively attired in governmint fours, an' fannin' himsilf with a bunch iv first morgedge bonds.

" Th' prayers f'r th' occasion, printed on negotyable paper, is disthributed among th' guests. Th' bride was delayed be th' crowd outside. Women screamed an' waved their handkerchefs, sthrong men cheered an' wept; an' 'twas not until th' polis had clubbed tin hardy pathrites to death that th' lady cud enther th' house where her fate was to be sealed. But fin'lly she med it; an' th' two happy, happy childher, whose sunshiny youth riprisinted five thousan' miles iv thrack, eight goold mines, wan hundherd millyion dollars' worth iv rollin' stock, an' a majority intherest in th' Chicago stock yards, was r-ready f'r th' nicissary thransfers that wud establish th' com-bination.

" Th' ceremony was brief, but intherestin'. Th' happy father foorced his way through dimon' stomachers; an' they was tears in his

eyes as he handed th' clargyman, whose name
was Murphy,— but he carried himsilf as
well as if he was used to it,— handed him a
check f'r tin millyion dollars. I don't blame
him. Divvle th' bit! Me own hear-rt is
har-rd an' me eyes ar-re dhry, but I'd break
down if I had to hand anny wan that much.
'I suppose th' check is good,' says th' clargyman. ''Tis certified,' says th' weepin'
father. 'Do ye take this check,' says th'
clargyman, 'to have an' to hold, until some
wan parts ye fr'm it?' he says. 'I do,' says
th' young man. 'Thin,' says th' clargyman,
'I see no reason why ye shudden't be marrid an' live comfortable,' he says. An' marrid
they were, in th' same ol' foolish way that
people's been marrid in f'r cinchries. 'Tis a
wondher to me th' ceremony ain't changed.
Th' time is comin', Hinnissy, whin mill-
yionaires 'll not be marrid be Father Murphy, but be th gov'nors iv th' stock exchange. They'll be put through th' clearin'
house, me faith, an' securities 'll be issued
be th' combination. Twinty-year, goold-

secured, four per cint. bonds iv mathrimony!
Aha, 'tis a joke that Chansy Depoo might 've
med!

"Th' crowd outside waited, cheerin' an'
fightin' th' polis. In this here land iv liberty an' akequality, Hinnissy, ivry man is as
good as ivry other man, except a polisman.
An' it showed how thrue th' people in New
York is to th' thraditions iv Jefferson that
divvle a wan iv thim 'd move away till th'
check 'd been passed fr'm father to son, an'
th' important part iv th' sacred ceremony
was over. Thin a few iv thim wint home to
cook dinner f'r their husbands, who was pre-
vinted be their jooties at th' gas-house fr'm
attindin' th' function. Th' rest raymained
an' see th' two gr-reat fortunes get into their
carredge, pursued be th' guests to th' amount
iv five hundhred millyions, peltin' thim with
seed pearls."

"Sure," said Mr. Hennessy, "mebbe
'twasn't as bad as th' pa-apers let on. Ye
can't always thrust thim."

"P'rhaps not," said Mr. Dooley. "Th'

pa-apers say, 'Two gr-reat fortunes united';
an', if that's it, they didn't need th' sarvices
iv a priest, but a lawyer an' a thrust com-
p'ny. P'rhaps, with all th' certyfied checks,
'twas two rale people that was marrid; an', if
that's so, it explains th' prisince if Father
Murphy."

THE DREYFUS CASE.

I.

"Th' scene was treemenjously excitin'. Th' little city iv Rennes was thronged with des'prit journalists that had pledged their fortunes an' their sacred honors, an' manny iv thim their watches, to be prisint an' protect th' public again th' degradin' facts. Niver since th' war in Cubia has so manny iv these brave fellows been gathered together at th' risk iv their lives fr'm overcrowdin' th' resthrants. No wan has iver sufficiently described th' turrors iv a corryspondint's life excipt th' corryspondints thimsilves. Gin'-rals an' other liars is rewarded. Th' corryspondint gets no credit. No wan will give him credit. Still he sticks to his post; an' on this pearlous day he was at Rennes, fightin' th' other corryspondints, or, if he was an English journalist, defindin' th' honor iv Fr-rance again hersilf. 'Tis a good thing for Fr-rance that there ar-re silf-sacrificin' men that don't undherstand her language,

to presint her vicious nature to th' English
an' American public.   Otherwise, Hinnissy,
she might think she was as good as th' rest
iv us.

"Well, while th' sthreets in Rennes was
packed with these dauntless souls, ar-rmed
with death-dealin' kodaks, there was a com-
motion near th' coort-house.   Was it a rivolution?   Was this th' beginnin' iv another
Saint Barth'mew's Day, whin th' degraded
passions in Fr-rance, pent up durin' three
hundherd years, 'd break forth again?   Was
it th' signal iv another div'lish outbreak
that 'd show th' thrue nature iv th' Fr-rinch
people, disgeezed behind a varnish iv ojoous
politeness which our waiters know nawthin'
about?   No, alas! alas! 'twas nawthin' a man
cud make more thin a column iv.   'Twas
th' ac-cursed janitor goin' in to open th'
degraded windows.   Abase th' janitor, abase
th' windows!   Fear followed uncertainty.
No wan knew what moment he might be
called upon to defind his life with his honor.
Suddenly th' brutal polisman who sthud on

gyard waved his hand.   What cud the brave
men do?   They were obliged to rethreat
in disordher.   But our special corryspondint
was able f'r to obtain a fine view of th'
thrillin' scene that followed.   First came th'
coort, weepin'.   They was followed be th'
gin'rals in th' Fr-rinch ar-rmy, stalwart, fearless men, with coarse, disagreeable faces.
Each gin'ral was attinded be his private body-
gyard iv thried and thrusted perjurers, an'
was followed be a wagon-load iv forgeries,
bogus affidavies, an' other statements iv
Major Estherhazy.   Afther thim come th'
former ministers iv th' Fr-rinch governmint,
makin' an imposin' line, which took three
hours passin' a given point.   As they
marched, it was seen that they were shyly
kickin' each other.

   " An interval iv silence followed, in which
cud be heard cries iv ' Abase Dhryfuss!' an'
' Abase Fr-rance!' an' thin come th' man
on whom th' lies iv all th' wurruld is cin-
thred.   Captain Dhryfuss plainly shows his
throubles, which have made him look tin

years younger. His raven hair is intirely
white; an' his stalwart frame, with th' shoulders thrown back, is stooped an' weary.
His haggard face was flushed with insolent
confidence, an' th' cowa'dice in his face
showed in his fearless eye. As he passed,
a young Fr-rinch sojer was with diff'culty
resthrained fr'm sthrikin' him an' embracin'
him with tears in his eyes.

"In th' coort-room th' scene baffled description. It was an inspirin' sight f'r th'
judges, whin they were awake. Row on row
iv journalists, sharpin' pencils an' slappin'
each other's faces, r-rose to th' ceilin'. Here
an' there cud be seen a brillyant uniform,
denotin' th' prisince iv th' London Times corryspondint. Th' lawn behind th' coort was
thronged with ex-mimbers iv th' Fr-rinch
governmint. Th' gin'ral staff, bein' witnesses
f'r th' prosecution, sat with th' coort: th'
pris'ner, not bein' able to find a chair, sat on
th' window-sill. His inthrest in th' proceedin's was much noticed, an' caused gr-reat
amusement. Ivrybody was talkin' about th'

mysteryous lady in white. Who is she?
Some say she is a Dhryfussard in th' imploy
iv Rothscheeld; others, that she is an agent
iv th' Anti-Semites. No wan has learned
her name. She says she is Madame Lucille
Gazahs, iv wan hundherd an' eight Rue le
Bombon, an' is a fav'rite iv th' Fr-rinch
stage. She is wan iv th' great mysthries
iv this ree-markable thrile.

" Afther th' coort had kissed th' witnesses,
th' proceedin's opined. 'Tis thrue, they
kiss each other. I wanst see a Fr-rinchman
go f'r to kiss a man be th' name iv Doherty,
that inthrajooced risolutions in favor iv
Fr-rance again Germany at a convintion.
Doherty thought he was afther his ear, an'
laid him out. But in Fr-rance 'tis diff'rent.
They begin be kissin', an' this thrile opined
this way.

" ' Pris'ner,' said th' prisident iv th' coort,
' th' eyes iv Fr-rance is upon us, th' honor
iv th' nation is at stake. Th' naytional de-
finces, th' integrity iv that ar-rmy upon
which Fr-rance must depind in time iv peace,

th' virtue iv public life, an' th' receipts iv
th' exposition is involved. Incidentally, ye
ar-re bein' thried. But why dhrag in matthers iv no importance? We ar-re insthructed, accordin' to th' pa-apers, be th'
Coort iv Cassation, to permit no ividince
that does not apply to your connection with
th' case. As sojers, we bow to th' superyor
will. We will follow out th' insthructions iv
th' supreme coort. We have not had time
to read thim, but we will look at thim
afther th' thrile. In th' mane time we will
call upon Gin'ral Merceer, that gallant man,
to tell us th' sthory iv his life.'

"'I obey, mon colonel,' says Gin'ral
Merceer, kissin' th' coort. 'Not to begin
too far back, an' to make a long sthory short,
I am an honest man, an' th' son iv an honest
man. I admit it.'

"'Good,' says th' prisident. 'D'ye rec-
ognize th' pris'ner?' 'I do,' says Gin'ral
Merceer, 'I seen him wanst dhrinkin' a shell
iv Munich beer in a caafe. [Marked sensation in th' coort, an' cries iv 'Abase la
bock.']·

" ' I says to mesilf thin, " This man is a
thraitor." But th' thrainin' iv a sojer makes
wan cautious. I determined to fortify mesilf with ividince. I put spies on this man,
this perfiejous wretch, an' discovered nawthin'.
I was paralyzed. An officer iv th' Fr-rinch
ar-rmy, an' nawthin' suspicyous about him !
Damnable ! I was with difficulty resthrained
fr'm killin' him. But I desisted. [Cries iv
' Shame ! '] I said to mesilf : " Th' honor iv
Fr-rance is at stake. Th' whole wurruld is
lookin' at me, at me, Bill Merceer. I will
go to bed an' think it over." I wint to bed.
Sleep, blessed sleep that sews up th' confused
coat-sleeve iv care, as th' perfiejous Shakspere [cries iv ' Conspuez Shakspere ! ']
says, dayscinded on me tired eyes. [The
coort weeps.] I laid aside me honor
[cries iv ' Brave gin'ral '] with me coat
[murmurs]. I slept.

" ' I dhreamed that I see th' German Impror playin' a Jew's-harp. [Cries iv ' Abase
Rothscheeld ! ' an' sensation.] I woke with
a vi'lent start, th' perspiration poorin' fr'm

me rugged brow. "Cap Dhryfuss is guilty,"
I cried. But no, I will confirm me ividince.
I darted into me r-red pants. I dhruv with
fury to th' home iv Madame Cleepathry, th'
cillibrated Agyptian asthrologist an' med'cin
woman. [Th' coort, 'We know her, she
supplies ividence to all Fr-rinch coorts.']
I tol' her me dhream. She projoosed a pack
iv cards. She tur-rned a r-red king an' a
black knave. "Th' Impror Willum an' Cap
Dhryfuss," I says, in a fury. I burst forth.
I had Cap Dhryfuss arristed. I dashed to
th' prisident. He was a-receivin' rayfusals
f'r a new cabinet. "I have found th' thraitor," says I. "Hush!" says he. "If th'
Impror Willum hears ye, he'll declare war,"
he says. I was stupefied. "Oh, my beloved
counthry!" I cried. "Oh, hivin!" I cried.
"What shall I do?" I cried. They was
not a minyit to lose. I disbanded th'
ar-rmy. I ordhered th' navy into dhry
dock. I had me pitcher took. I wint
home an' hid in th' cellar. F'r wan night
Fr-rance was safe.'

"They was hardly a dhry eye in th' house whin th' gin'ral paused. Th' coort wept. Th' audjience wept. Siv'ral of th' minor journalists was swept out iv th' room in th' flood. A man shovellin' coal in th' cellar sint up f'r an umbrella. Th' lawn shook with th' convulsive sobs iv th' former ministers. Gin'ral Merceer raised his damp face, an' blew a kiss to a former minister at wan iv th' windows, an' resumed his tistimony."

II.

"'It was about this time or some years later,' continues Gin'ral Merceer, 'that I received ividince iv th' Cap's guilt. I made it mesilf. It was a letter written be me fr'm th' Cap to a German grocer, askin' f'r twinty r-rounds iv sausage. [Turmoil in the coort.] It was impossible, mon colonel, that this here letter cud have been written be Estherhazy. In th' first place he was in Paris at th' time, in th' sicond place he was in London. Th' letter is not in his handwritin', but in th' handwritin' iv Colonel Pat th' Clam. Thin again I wrote th' letter mesilf. Thin who cud 've written it? It must 've been Cap Dhryfuss. [Cheers fr'm th' coort.] I give me reasons as they occurred to me: First, th' Armeenyan athrocities; sicond, th' risignation iv Gin'ral Alger; third, th' marriage iv Prince Lobengula; fourth, th' scarcity iv sarvint girls in th' sooburban towns; fifth, th' price iv gas. [Cries iv 'Abase th' price iv gas!'] I thank th' aujience. I will raysume where I left off. I was speakin' iv Gin'ral Guns. I met him on th' sthreet. Th' moon was clear in th' sky. I says, "Guns," I says, "lave us go down to Hogan's, an' I'll buy ye a tub iv obsceenthe." As we sthrolled through th' bullyvard, I saw a man that looked like a German dhrivin' a cab. I was overcome with terror. I ran madly home, followed be Guns. It was a week befure I cud hold a glass iv obsceenthe without spillin' th' liquor. Shortly afther this, or it may've been tin years befure, or it may niver have occurred [the coort, 'Spoken like a Fr-rinchman an' a sojer'], in th' middle iv July a man tol' me that the divine Sara [wild an' continyous applause, cries iv 'Sara foriver!'] was about to projooce th' immortal play iv "Omlet" [cheers] be th' wretched Shakspere [hisses]. Cud annything be clearer? I will detain th' coort not longer thin a day while I give me opinyon on this marvellous performance.'

"Cap Dhryfuss was settin' on th' win-

dow-sill, whistlin' 'Garry Owen,' an' makin'
faces at th' gallant corryspondint iv th' Daily
Wrongs iv Man.   At this point he cried
out laughingly: ' I will not conthradict th'
gin'ral.   I will say he lies.   I saw th' letter
mesilf, an' that man was Esterhazy.'   [Sen-
sation.]

"' Let me ask this canal iv a Jew a question,' says th' corryspondint iv th' evening
Rothscheeld Roaster, a Fr-rinchman be th'
name iv Sol Levi.

"' Ask it,' says Cap Dhryfuss.

"' You are a despicable thraitor,' says th'
gallant corryspondint.   [Sensation.]

"' Th' pris'nor must answer,' says th'
coort.   ' It is now nearly six o'clock iv th'
mornin', an' time to get up an' dhress.'

"' I refuse to make anny commint,' says
Cap Dhryfuss.

" The pris'nor's remark, uttered in tones
iv despair, caused gr-reat emotion in th'
aujience.   There were angry cries iv ' Lynch
him!' an' all eyes were tur-rned to th' Cap.

"' Silence!' roared th' coort, bendin' a

stern, inflexible look on th' pris'nor. 'This is a coort iv justice. We ar-re disposed f'r to grant ivry indulgence; but, if outsiders persist in intherferin' with these proceedin's,' he says, 'we'll expel thim fr'm th' r-room. What does th' pris'ner think this is?'

"'I thought it was a thrile,' says th' Cap; 'but, be th' number iv vet'ran journalists here, it must be th' openin' iv a new hotel.'

"'Not another wurrud,' says th' coort, 'or ye'll be fired out. No wan shall insult th' honest, hard-wurrukin', sober, sensible journalists iv Fr-rance. Not if this coort knows it. Ye bet ye, boys, th' coort is with ye. Th' press is th' pallajeen iv our liberties. Gin'ral Merceer will raysume his tistimony. He was speakin' of th' game iv goluf.'

"'Perhaps I'd betther sing it,' says th' gin'ral.

"'I'll play an accompanymint f'r ye on th' flute,' says th' prisident iv th' coort. 'While Gin'ral Merceer is proceedin' with his remarks, call Colonel Pat th' Clam, who is sick an' can't come. Swear Gin'ral Billot, Gin'ral Boisdeffer, Gin'ral Chammy, an' th' former mimbers iv th' governmint.'

" ' I object to thim bein' sworn,' says Matther Blamange.

" ' They must be sworn,' says th' prisident. ' How th' divvle can they perjure thimsilves if they ain't sworn? An' who ar-re ye, annyhow?'

" ' I'm th' counsel f'r th' pris'ner,' says Matther Blamange. ' Get out ye'ersilf,' says Matther Blamange. ' I'm as good a man as ye ar-re. I will ask that gintleman who jest wint out the dure, Does it pay to keep up appearances?' [Groans.]

" ' Gin'ral Billot,' says th' prisident, ' what d'ye know about this infernal case which is broodin' like a nightmare over our belovid counthry, an' gettin' us up ivry mornin' befure milkin' time?'

" ' Nawthin' at all,' says Gin'ral Billot.

" ' Nayther do I,' says th' prisident. ' But I think th' Cap's guilty.'

"'I'm glad to hear ye say that,' says th'
gin'ral. 'If ye didn't, I'd rayjooce ye to
th' r-ranks to-morrah. I niver see th' man
befure; an', be hivins, I don't want to see him
again. But I have a letter here fr'm him,
askin' me if he cud knock off wurruk at
four o'clock to go to his aunt's fun'ral.'

"'Cap,' says th' prisident, 'what ye got to
say to this? Did ye write th' letter?'

"'I did,' says th' Cap.

"'Throw it out thin,' says th' prisident.
'We must be guided be th' laws iv ividence.
Th' witness will confine himself to forgeries.
Have ye e'er a forgery about ye'er clothes,
mon gin'ral?'

"'I wish to confront th' witness,' says
Matther Blamange.

"'Sit down,'" says th' prisident.

"'D'ye raymimber meetin' me at dinner
at Moosoo de Bozoo's. It was years ago,
durin' th' time iv Napolyeon, befure th' big
fire? If I raymimber right, we had peas.
Wasn't it a lovely night? Oh dear, oh
dear, gintlemen iv th' press an' mon prisi-

dent, ye ought to have been there. Well,
I says to Gin'ral Billot, I says, " Gin'ral," I
says, " how ar-re ye, annyhow." An' the
gin'ral replies, " F'r an ol' man, well." I
made up me mind thin that th' Cap was
innocent, an' this was befure he was born.

" ' Me distinguished colleague in th' thrile
iv this case, th' editor iv wan iv th' Paris
papers,' says th' prisident, ' has received a
letter fr'm th' military attachay or spy iv th'
Impror iv Austhrich, sayin' that he did not
write th' letter referred to be Prisident
Kruger, an', if he did, it's a forgery. But
what cud ye ixpict ? I will throw both letters
into the secret dossier.'

" ' What's that ? ' says Matther Blamange.

" ' It's a collection iv pomes wrote to th'
Paris papers be spies,' says th' prisident.
' Call Colonel Peekhart, if th' others ar-re
not through. What, you again, Peekhart ?
Set down, sir.'

" ' Gintlemen iv Fr-rance,' says Colonel
Peekhart. ' Unaccustomed as I am to public speakin', I wish to addhress ye a few

wurruds on th' situation iv th' poor in China.'

"'Assassin!' hisses th' coort.

"'Canal!' says Matther Blamange.

"At this moment th' door was burst open; an' an ex-Prisidint iv Fr-rance come boundin' in, an', r-rushin' up th' steps iv th' thrybune, smacked Gin'ral Merceer in th' eye. Th' gr-reatest rayspict was shown f'r th' former chief magistrate iv th' raypublic. No wan shot at him. He was white with rage. 'Th' honor iv Fr-rance is at stake,' he says. 'Our counthry lies prostrate in th' mud. I must presarve th' dignity iv me high office; but, if Gin'ral Merceer will step out into th' back yard, I'll beat his head off. I don't know annything about this accursed case. It was all referred to me whin I was Prisident. I am here to see that th' honor iv me high office is not assailed. I protest I did not say what an anonymous corry-spondint in to-night's Sore says I said. I did me jooty. Whin I saw th' ar-rmy dis-organized an' Fr-rance beset be foreign foes,

I raysigned. What was I to do? Was I to stay in office, an' have me hat smashed in ivry time I wint out to walk? I tell ye, gintlemen, that office is no signcure. Until hats are made iv cast iron, no poor man can be Prisident iv Fr-rance. But I was not speakin' iv th' Dhryfuss case.'

" ' Don't dare to mintion that matter in this coort,' says th' prisident. ' I'm surprised a man iv ye'er intilligence'd thry to dhrag in exthranyous matther, whin th' honor iv th' ar-rmy is at stake. Gin'ral Merceer, stand beside this witness. Now both speak at wanst! Annybody else that has annything to say, lave him say it now, so it won't be heard.'

" ' Mon colonel,' says a former minister iv th' Fr-rinch governmint, who was th' polisman at th' dure, ' Judge Crazy th' Boorepare is here, demandin' to be heard.'

" ' Gr-reat hivins!' says th' coort; an' they wint out through th' windows.

" That night they was gr-reat excitement in Rennes. Th' citizens dhrivin home their

cows cud har'ly make their way through th'
excited throngs on th' sthreet. Th' corryspondints iv th' English papers do not dare
to go to bed befure nine o'clock on account
iv rumors iv a gin'ral massacre. Madame
Sara Bernhardt gave a magnificint performance at th' theaytre, an' was wildly cheered.
It was believed in London, Budapesth,
Posen, New York, Cookham, an' Upper
Sandusky that Fr-rance is about to perish.
As I go to press, th' news has excited no
commint in Fr-rance."

III.

" WHILE th' thrillin' scenes I'm tellin' ye about is goin' on, Hinnissy, worse is bein' enacted in beautiful Paris. In that lovely city with its miles an' miles iv sparklin' resthrants,— la belly Paree, as Hogan 'd say, — th' largest American city in th' wurruld, a rivolution's begun. If ye don't believe it, read th' pa-apers. They've arrested a pote. That was all r-right; f'r Fr-rance is sufferin' fr'm too much pothry that 'll scan, as Hogan says, an' too much morality that won't. They ought to be a rule f'r th' polis to pinch anny pote caught poting between th' hours iv twelve an' twelve. But th' mistake th' chief iv th' polis made was to r-run in a butcher at th' same time. What th' butcher done I dinnaw; but anny-how they accused him iv wantin' to pole-axe th' governmint; an' they thrun him into a cell. Now th' butcher he had a frind be th' name iv Guerin,— an Irish name it is,

but this la-ad don't appear to be wan iv
us,— Jools Guerin. He was wanst in th'
thripe business; but he is now r-runnin' a
newspaper, like most iv th' people iv Fr-rance.
As a thripe butcher, his circulation was larger
an' among a betther class than his newspaper. Bein' a la-ad with a fine sinse iv
gratichood, an' havin' been wanst fed an'
clothed be a Jew man, he calls his pa-aper
th' Anti-Jew; an' its principle is, whin ye
see a Jew, hand him a crack in th' jaw. 'Tis
a good principle, though I wanst knew a
man be th' name iv Solomon Felsenthal,
that was known in th' ring as Mike Gal-
legher, th' Tipp'rary Cyclone, as a thribute
to th' feelin's iv th' pathrons iv spoort; an',
if Jools had thried to carry out his platform
with Solly, they'd be no siege in Fort
Chabrool. Not anny. That Jew man 'd
been champeen iv th' wurruld if all iv him
cud 've kept out iv close quarthers with th'
man again him.

 " I don't quarrel with Jools' feelin's, mind
ye. 'Tis th' histhry iv th' wurruld that th'

Jews takes our watches fr'm us be tin per cint
a month, an' we take thim back be means iv
a jimmy an' a piece iv lead pipe.   They're
on'y two known methods iv finance,— bank-
in' an' burglary.   Th' Jews has th' first
down fine, but all th' rest iv th' wurruld is
at home in th' second.   So Jools 's all
r-right as far as he goes.   But he don't go
far.

"Well, whin Jools hear-rd that his frind
th' butcher was sloughed up, he wint fairly
wild.   He says to himsilf, he says, 'I'll go
home,' he says, 'an' defy th' governmint,'
he says.   'I'll start a rivolution,' he says.
'But,' he says, 'I must first notify th' polis,'
he says, 'so's to prevint disordher,' he says.
So he wint to th' chief iv polis, who was an
ol' frind iv his,— they was in th' same newspaper office or thripe dairy or something,—
an' th' chief kissed Jools, an' asked him what
he cud do f'r him.   'I wish,' said Jools,
'ye'd sind down tin or a dozen good men
in uniform an' a few detectives in citizen's
clothes,' he says.

"'I've asked some ladies an' gintlemen to a five o'clock rivolution at my house,' he says; 'an' I'd like to be sure they'll be no disordher,' he says. 'Well,' says th' chief, ''twill not be aisy,' he says. 'Ye see th' prisident—I f'rget his name—has been asked to go to th' r-races with some frinds,' he says; 'an' they will prob'bly thry to kill him,' he says. 'We can't play anny fav'-rites here,' he says. 'We have to protect th' low as well as th' high,' he says. 'If annything happens to this man, th' case is li'ble to be taken up be th' ex-prisidents' as-sociation; an' they're num'rous enough to make throuble f'r us,' he says. 'But,' he says, 'I'll do what I can f'r ye, me ol' frind,' he says. 'Give us th' best ye have,' says Jools; 'an', if ye've nawthin' to do afther ye close up, ye might dhrop in,' he says, 'an' have a manifesto with us,' he says. 'Come just as ye ar-re,' he says. ''Tis an informal rivolution,' he says.

"An' away he wint. At sharp five o'clock th' rivolution begun. Th' sthreets

was dinsely packed with busy journalists,
polis, sojers, an' fash'nably dhressed ladies
who come down fr'm th' Chang's All Easy
in motocycles. There was gr-reat excitement as Jools come to th' windy an' pinned
a copy iv his vallyable journal on th' sill,
accompanied be a thrusty liftnant wavin' a
statement iv th' circulation iv th' Anti-Jew.
Jools at this moment was a tur-rble sight.
He was dhressed fr'm head to foot in Har-
veyized, bomb-proof steel, with an asbestos
rose in his buttonhole. Round his waist
was sthrapped four hundherd rounds iv ca't-
ridges an' eight days' provisions. He car-
rid a Mauser rifle on each shoulder, a
machine gun undher wan ar-rm, a dinnymite
bomb undher another, an' he was smoking
a cigareet. ' Ladies an' gintlemen,' he says,
' I'm proud an' pleased to see ye prisint in
such lar-rge numbers at th' first rivolution iv
th' prisint season,' he says. ' With th' kind
permission iv th' hated polis undher th'
di-rection iv me good frind an' fellow-jour-
nalist, Loot Franswoo Coppere, an' th'

ar-rmy, f'r whose honor ivry Fr-renchman 'll lay down his life, th' siege will now begin. We will not,' he says, 'lave this house till we have driven ivry cur-rsed Cosmypollitan or Jew,' he says, 'fr'm this noble land iv th' br-rave an' home iv th' flea,' he says. 'Veev Fr-rance!' he says. 'Veev Jools Guerin!' he says. 'Conspuez Rothscheeld!' he says. 'It's ye'er move, Loot,' he says to th' polisman.

"'I defer to th' ar-rmy whose honor is beyond reproach,' says th' polisman, 'or recognition,' he says. 'Veev l'army!' he says.

"'Thank ye,' says Gin'ral Bellow, salutin'. 'I will do me jooty. Man can do no more,' he says. 'Jools,' he says, 'surrinder,' he says. 'Ye cannot longer hol' out,' he says. 'Ye have provisions on'y f'r eight years.'

"'We will remain till th' last wan iv us perishes iv indigestion,' says Jools.

"'Thin I must take sthrong measures,' says th' gin'ral. 'At a given signal we will storm th' house, bate down th' dures, smash in th' roofs, cut off th' gas, poison th' wather supply, back up th' sewer, break th' windys, an' r-raise th' rint.' "

" ' Do ye'er worst,' says Jools, proudly.

" ' Thin,' says th' gin'ral, imprissively, ' if these measures do not suffice, I will suspind th' deliv'ry iv th' mails,' he says.

" ' Miscreant ! ' cries Jools, tur-rnin' white. ' An' this is called a merciful governmint,' he says. ' Mong doo,' he says, ' what cr-rimes will not Fr-rinchmen commit again' Fr-rinchmen ! ' he says. ' But,' he says, ' ye little know us, if ye think we can be quelled be vi'lence,' he says. ' I have a last card,' he says. ' I refuse to give th' signal,' he says.

" ' Thin,' says th' gin'ral, tur-rnin' away with tears in his eyes, ' we must adopt other measures.'

" ' Very well,' says Jools. ' But mark wan thing,— that, if ye attempt to make me ridiculous, ye shall suffer.'

" ' I assure ye, mong editor,' says th' gin'ral, earnestly, ' that th' governmint will not make ye anny more ridiculous than it makes itsilf,' says he.

" ' Me honor is satisfied,' says Jools. ' Do ye'er worst,' he says.

" At eight o'clock th' minister iv war arrived, an' took command. He ordhered up twinty rig'mints iv cav'lry, tin batthries iv artillery, an' two divisions iv fut sojers. It was his intintion to sind th' cav'lry in over th' roofs, while th' army carried th' front stoop, protected be fire fr'm th' heavy artillery, while th' Fr-rinch navy shelled th' back dure. But this was seen to be impossible, because th' man that owned th' wineshop next dure, he said 'twud dhrive away custom. All th' sthreets f'r miles ar-round was blockaded without effect. Th' fire departmint was called to put Jools out, but wather niver touched him. Th' sewer gang wint down an' blocked th' dhrains, an' Jools soon had inspiration f'r a year's writin'. At last accounts th' garrison was still holdin' out bravely again a witherin' fire iv canned food, lobsters, omelets, an' hams. A brave gossoon in th' Sivinth Artill'ry did partic'- larly effective wurruk, hur-rlin' a plate iv scrambled eggs acrost th' sthreet without spillin' a dhrop, an' is now thrainin' a pie like mother used to make on th' first windy iv th' sicond flure. It is reported that th' minister iv war at four o'clock to-morrow mornin' will dhrop a bundle iv copies iv Jools' paper through th' chimbley. Whin he opens th' windy, a pome be Paul Deroulede 'll be read to him. This is again th' articles iv war, but th' case is desp'rate.

" But I was thinkin', Hinnissy, as I walked down th' Roo Chabrool, how I'd like to see a Chicago polisman come sthrollin' along with his hat on th' back iv his head. I don't love Chicago polismen. They seem to think ivry man's head's as hard as their own. But I'd give forty-three francs, or eight dollars an' sixty cints iv our money, if th' Fr-rinch governmint 'd sind f'r Jawnny Shea, an' ask him to put down this here rivolution. Th' nex' day they'd move th' office iv th' Anti-Seemite Society to th' morgue."

THE DREYFUS CASE.

IV.

"WELL, Hinnissy, to get back to Rennes. Whin I left off, th' air was full iv rumors iv an approachin' massacree. It was still full at daybreak. Exthraordinney measures was adopted to provide again disturbance. Th' gyard was doubled, an' both polismen had al! they cud do to keep th' crowd in ordher. Th' English an' American journalists appeared at th' thrile wrapped up in th' flags iv their rayspictive counthries. All th' Jews, excipt th' owners iv anti-Jew papers fr'm Paris, wore heavy masks an' kep' their hands in their pockets. At four o'clock th' prisident called th' audjience to disordher, an', havin' disentangled Gin'ral Merceer an' a former president iv th' raypublic, demanded if Moosoo Bertillon was in th' room.

"'Here,' says that gr-reat janius, descindin' fr'm th' roof in a parachute. Ye know Bertillon. Ye don't? Iv coorse ye do, Hinnissy. He's th' la-ad that invinted th'

system iv ditictive wurruk med aisy that
they use down in th' Cintral Polis Station.
I mind wanst, afther 'twas inthrojooced, th'
loot says to Andy Rohan,— he's a sergeant
now, be hivins ! — he says, ' Go out,' he says,
' an' fetch in Mike McGool, th' safe robber,'
he says. ' Here's his description,' he says :
' eyelashes, eight killomethres long ; eyes,
blue an' assymethrical ; jaw, bituminous ;
measuremint fr'm abaft th' left ear to base iv
maxillory glan's, four hectograms ; a r-red
scar runnin' fr'm th' noomo-gasthric narve
to th' sicond dorsal verteebree,' he says.
'Tis so. I have th' description at home in
th' cash dhrawer. Well, Andy come in
about six o'clock that night, lookin' as
though he'd been thryin' to r-run a fut race
acrost a pile iv scrap ir'n ; an' says he,
' Loot,' he says, ' I've got him,' he says.
" I didn't take th' measuremints,' he says,
' because, whin I pulled out th' tape line,
he rowled me eighty hectograms down th'
sthreet,' he says. ' But 'tis Mike McGool,'
he says. ' I don't know annything about

his noomo-gasthric narves,' he says, ' but I
reco'nized his face,' he says.   ' I've r-run
him in fifty times,' he says.

   " Bertillon, besides bein' a profissor iv
detictives, is a handwritin' expert, which is
wan iv th' principal industhrees iv Fr-rance
at th' prisint time.   He was accompanied be
a throop iv assistants carryin' a camera, a
mutoscope, a magic lantern, a tib iv dye, a
telescope, a calceem light, a sextant, a com-
pass, a thermometer, a barometer, a thrunk-
ful iv speeches, a duplicate to th' Agyptian
obelisk, an ink-eraser, an' a rayceipt f'r
makin' goold out iv lead pipe.

   " ' Well, sir,' says Bertillon, ' what d'ye
want ? '

   " ' Nawthin',' says th' coort.   ' Didn't ye
ask to be called here ? '

   " ' No,' says Bertillon, ' an' ye didn't ask
me, ayther.   I come.   Ye said jus' now,
Why do I believe th' Cap's guilty ?   I will
show ye.   In th' spring iv ninety-five or th'
fall iv sixty-eight, I disraymimber which,
Gin'ral Merceer ' —

" ' Ye lie,' says Gin'ral Merceer, coldly.

" ' —— called on me; an' says he, " Bertillon," he says, " ye'er fam'ly's been a little
cracked, an' I thought to ask ye to identify
this letther which I've jus' had written be
a frind iv mine, Major Estherhazy," he says.
" I don't care to mintion who we suspect;
but he's a canal Jew in th' artillery, an' his
name's Cap Dhryfuss," he says. " It's not
aisy," I says; " but, if th' honor iv th' ar-rmy's
at stake, I'll thry to fix th' raysponsibility,"
I says. An' I wint to wurruk. I discovered in th' first place that all sentences begun with capitals, an' they was a peryod at
th' end iv each. This aroused me suspi-
cions. Clearly, this letther was written be
a Jew. Here I paused, f'r I had no sam-
ples iv th' Cap's writin' to compare with it.
So I wrote wan mesilf. They was much th'
same. " Sure," says I, " th' Cap's guilty," I
says. But how did he do it? I thried a
number iv experiments. I first laid down
over th' letther a piece of common tissue
paper. Th' writin' was perfectly plain

through this. Thin I threw it on a screen eighteen hands high. Thin I threw it off. Thin I set it to music, an' played it on a flute. Thin I cooked it over a slow fire, an' left it in a cool airy place to dhry. In an instant it flashed over me how th' forgery was done. "Th' Cap first give it to his little boy to write. Thin he had his wife copy it in imitation iv Macchew Dhryfuss's handwritin'. Thin Macchew wrote it in imitation iv Estherhazy. Thin th' Cap had it put on a typewriter, an' r-run through a wringer. Thin he laid it transversely acrost a piece of wall paper; an', whereiver th' key wurrud sponge-cake appeared, he was thereby able f'r to make a sympathic lesion, acquirin' all th' characteristics iv th' race, an' a dam sight more."

"'I follow ye like a horse afther a hay wagon,' says th' prisident, 'hungrily, but unsatisfacthrly. Ye do not prove that th' throuble was symotic, mong expert.'

"'Parfictly,' says Moosoo Bertillon. 'I will have me assistants put up a screen, an' on this I will projooce ividince' —

"' Go away,' says th' president. ' Call Colonel Prystalter. Mong colonel, ye thraitor, describe th' conversation ye had with Colonel Schneider, th' honorable but lyin' spy or confidential envoy iv th' vin'rable Impror iv Austhrich, may th' divvle fly way with him ! But mind ye, ye must mintion no names.'

"' I know no man more honest,' says th' witness.

"' Thin your acquaintance is limited to ye'ersilf,' says Gin'ral Merceer.

"' Colonel Schneider,' says th' witness, ' th' Austhrich,—whom I will designate, f'r fear iv internaytional entanglements, merely as Colonel Schneider,— says to me, he says : " Th' letther pretindin' to be fr'm me is a forgery." " How's that ? " says I. " Didn't ye write an' sign it ? " I says. " I did," says he. " But some wan else sint it to th' pa-apers."

"' Thin 'tis clearly a forgery,' says th' prisident.

"' I wish to ask this witness wan question,' says Gin'ral Merceer. ' Was it th' Robin shell or th' day befure ? '

" ' My answer to that,' says th' witness, ' is decidedly, Who ? '

" ' Thin,' says Gin'ral Merceer, ' all I can say is, this wretch's tistimony is all a pack iv lies.'

" ' Hol' on there ! ' calls a voice from th' aujience.

" ' What d'ye want ? ' says th' prisident.

" ' I'm th' corryspondint iv th' Georgia Daily Lyncher, an' I can't undherstand a wurrud ye say. I've lost me dictionary. Th' people iv th' State iv Georgia mus' not be deprived iv their information about th' scand'lous conduct iv this infamious coort.'

" ' Thrue,' says th' prisident. ' Fr-rance 'd soon perish if Georgia shud thransfer its intherest fr'm Fr-rinch coorts to its own sacred timples iv justice. Perhaps some confrere 'll lind th' distinguished gazabo a copy iv his Ollendorff. Manewhile ' —

" ' Mong prisident,' says a white-faced polisman, ' Judge Crazy the Boore ' —

" ' Gr-reat hivins ! ' cried th' prisident. ' Thin th' quarantine at Oporto is a farce.'

An' he plunged into th' seething mass iv handwritin' experts an' ex-prisidents iv th' raypublic in th' coort-yard below."

THE DREYFUS CASE.

V.

"An' I was thinkin', Hinnissy" (Mr. Dooley said in conclusion), "as I set in that there coort, surrounded be me fellow-journalists, spies, perjurers, an' other statesmen, that I'd give four dollars if th' president iv th' coort 'd call out, 'Moosoo Dooley, take th' stand.'

"'Here,' says I; an' I 'd thread me way with dignity through th' Fr-rinch gin'rals an' ministers on th' flure, an' give me hand to th' prisident to kiss. If he went anny further, I'd break his head. No man 'll kiss me, Hinnissy, an' live. What's that ye say? He wudden't want to? Well, niver mind.

"'Here,' says I, 'mong colonel, what d'ye want with me?'

"'What d'ye know about this case, mong bar-tinder.'

"'Nawthin',' says I. 'But I know as much as annywan else. I know more thin most iv thim la-ads down below; f'r I can't undherstand a wurrud ye say, so I'm onable,' I says, 'f'r to make mistakes. I won't give anny tistimony, because 'twud be out iv place in this sacred timple devoted to th' practice iv orathry,' I says; 'but I can make as good a speech as annywan, an' here goes.'

" Gin'ral Merceer.— ' May I ask this polluted witness wan question?'

" Th' Witness.— ' Set down, ye infamious ol' polthroon!' says I. ' Set down an' pondher ye'er sins,' I says. ' If ye had ye'er dues, ye'd be cooprin' a bar'l in th' pinitinchry. If ye're afraid iv th' Impror Willum, be hivins, ye want to be afraid iv th' Impror Dooley; f'r he's Dutch, an' I ain't. I'll raysume me speech. Lady an' Gintlemen, prisoner at th' bar, freeman that ought to be there, lawyers, gin'rals, ex-prisidents, former mimbers iv th' cabinet, an' you, me gin'rous confreres iv th' wurruld's press, I come fr'm a land where injustice is unknown, where ivry man is akel befure th' law, but some are bether thin others behind it, where th' accused always has a fair thrile ayether,' I says, 'in th' criminal coort or at th' coroner's inquest,' I says. 'I have just been in another counthry where such conduct as we've witnessed here wud be unknown at a second thrile,' I says, 'because they have no second thriles,' I says. 'We Anglo-Saxons ar-re th' salt iv th' earth, an' don't ye f'rget it, boys. All our affairs ar-re in ordher. We convict no innocent men an' very few guilty wans, perjury is unknown amongst us, we have no military scandals, an' our private life is beyond rebuke. So we have th' time an' th' inclination to study th' vile offences iv our neighbors, an' give thim advice free iv cost. An' that is why I'm here to-day in this degraded counthry to tell ye what's th' matther with ye an' what ye ought to do.

"'An' this is me opinyon : I don't think Cap. Dhryfus wr-rote th' borderoo. I think he was th' on'y man in Fr-rance that didn't. But I ain't got as high an opinyon iv th' Cap

as I had.   I ain't no purity brigade; but, th'
older I get, th' more I think wan wife's
enough f'r anny man, an' too manny f'r
some.   They was a time, Cap, whin 'twas
seryously thought iv takin' ye fr'm th'
Divvle's Own Island an' makin' ye prisident
iv th' Women's Rescue League.   But I'm
afraid, Cap, ye're disqualified f'r that position be what we've heard fr'm ye'er own lips
durin' th' thrile.   Ye lost a good job.   Thin
there ar-re some other things about ye I
don't undherstand.   I can't make out what
ye meant be pretindin' to go to It'ly an'
doublin' back into Germany; an' I wish f'r
me own peace iv mind all ye'er explana-
tions 'd mate.   But, sure, if ivry man that
was too free with his affections was to be sint
to th' Divvle's Own Island, they'd have to
build an intinsion to that far-famed winther
resort.   An' if suspicyous actions was proof
iv guilt, mong colonel, ye'd have th' mimbers iv th' gin'ral staff sthrung up in as
manny cages as ye see at th' Zoo-illogical
Gardens [laughter an' cries iv 'Veev
Dooley!']

"'Th' throuble is, mong colonel, lady an' gintlemen, that it ain't been Cap Dhryfuss that's been on thrile, but th' honor iv th' nation an' th' honor iv th' ar-rmy. If 'twas th' Cap that was charged, ye'd say to him, "Cap, we haven't anny proof again ye; but we don't like ye, an' ye'll have to move on." An' that 'd be th' end iv th' row. The Cap 'd go over to England an' go into th' South African minin' business, an' become what Hogan calls "A Casey's bellows." But, because some la-ad on th' gin'ral staff got caught lyin' in th' start an' had to lie some more to make th' first wan stick, an' th' other gin'rals had to jine him f'r fear he might compromise thim if he wint on telling his fairy stories, an' they was la-ads r-runnin' newspapers in Paris that needed to make a little money out iv th' popylation, ye said, "Th' honor iv th' Fr-rinch people an' th' honor iv th' Fr-rinch ar-rmy is on thrile"; an' ye've put thim in th' dock instead iv th' Cap. Th' honor iv Fr-rance is all right, me boy, an' will be so

long as th' Fr-rinch newspapers is not read
out iv Paree,' I says. 'An', if th' honor iv
th' Fr-rinch ar-rmy can stand thim pants
that ye hew out iv red flannel f'r thim, a
little threachery won't injure it at all,' I says.
'Yes,' says I, 'th' honor iv Fr-rance an' th'
honor iv th' ar-rmy'll come out all r-right,'
I says; 'but it wudden't do anny harm f'r
to sind th' honor iv th' Fr-rinch gin'rals to
th' laundhry,' I says. 'I think ye'd have
to sind Gin'ral Merceer's to th' dyer's,' I
says. 'Ye niver can take out th' spots, an'
it might as well all be th' same color,' I says.
'Mong colonel,' I says imprissively, 'so
long as ivry man looks out f'r his own
honor, th' honor iv th' counthry'll look out
f'r itsilf,' I says. 'No wan iver heard iv a
nation stealin' a lead pipe or committin' perjury,' I says. ''Tis th' men that makes up
th' nation that goes in f'r these diversions,'
I says. 'I'd hate to insure again burglars
th' naytional honor that was guarded be that
ol' gazabo,' says I, indicatin' Merceer with
th' toe iv me boot.

" 'That's wan point. They's another, mong colonel. Ye're all afraid. That's th' truth iv th' matther. Ye're like a lot iv ol' women that thinks ivry time th' shutter creaks burglars is goin' to break into th' house. Ye're afraid iv Rothscheeld, an' th' Impror iv Germany, an' th' Dook d'Orleans, Vik Bonaparte, an' Joe Chamberlain, an' Bill McKinley. Be hivins, I believe ye're even afraid iv Gin'ral Otis! Ye're afraid iv th' newspapers, ye're afraid iv Jools Guerin, ye're afraid iv a pote, even whin he is not ar-rmed with his pothry, an' ye're afraid iv each other. Brace up! be men! If I was a Fr-rinchman, I'd be afraid iv no man but th' cab-dhrivers; an' I wudden't be afraid iv thim long, f'r I'd be a cab-dhriver mesilf.

" 'Wan thing more, an' thin me tistimony's over. Ye want me advice. Ye didn't ask f'r it. If I was prisident iv this coort-martial, I'd say to Cap Dhryfuss: "Cap, get out. Ye may not be a thraitor, but ye're worse. Ye're become a bore." '

An' I'd give him money enough to lave th' counthry. Thin I'd sind th' gin'ral staff off to some quiet counthry village where they'd be free fr'm rumors iv war, an' have nawthin' else to do but set around in rockin'-chairs an' play with th' cat. Thin I'd cut th' cable to England; an' thin I'd gather all the journalists iv Paris together, an' I'd say, "Gintlemen," I'd say, "th' press is th' palajeem iv our liberties," I'd say ; "but our liberties no longer requires a palajeem," I'd say. "This wan, whativer it means, is frayed at th' risbands, an' th' buttonholes is broken, annyhow," I'd say. "I've bought all iv ye tickets to Johannisberg," I'd say, "an' ye'll be shipped there to-night," I'd say. "Ye'er confreres iv that gr-reat city is worn out with their exertions, an' ye'll find plenty iv wurruk to do. In fact, those iv ye that're anti-Seemites 'll niver lack imployment," I'd say. "Hinceforth Fr-rance will be free — fr'm th' likes iv ye," I'd say. An' th' nex' mornin' Paris 'd awake ca'm an' peaceful, with no newspapers, an' there 'd be more room in our own papers f'r th' base-ball news,' says I.

" ' But, mong liquor dealer, what ye pro-pose 'd depopylate France,' says th' prisident.

" ' If that's th' case,' says I, ' Fr-rance ought to be depopylated,' I says. ' I've been thinkin' that's th' on'y way it can be made fit to live in f'r a man fr'm Chicago, where th' jambons come fr'm,' says I, lavin' th' stand."

" Arrah, what ar-re ye talkin' about?" de-manded Mr. Hennessy. " Ye niver got a peek in th' dure."

" What have you been doin'?" Mr. Dooley asked, disregarding the interruption.

" I wint out to see th' rowlin' mills," said Mr. Hennessy. " They have a very good plant; an' a man be th' name iv Mechell Onnessy or Mike Hennessy, a cousin iv mine that come over th' Fenian time with Stevens, is boss iv a gang. He speaks Fr-rinch like a boardin'-school. I talked with wan iv th' la-ads through him.

"Did ye ask him about th' Dhryfuss case?" asked Mr. Dooley, eagerly.

"I did."

"What did he say?"

"He said he niver heerd of it."